Catalogue of Paintings

Volume III

English and European
19th and 20th centuries

The Reserve Collection

City of York Art Gallery
York

MCMLXXIV

CONTENTS

INTRODUCTION

This third and final volume of the catalogue of oil paintings in York City Art Gallery comprises two unequal sections. The first, and by far the more important, catalogues 230 nineteenth- and twentieth-century English and European paintings; the second provides summary descriptions of a further 300 paintings which constitute the Gallery's total reserve collection (regardless of date or place of origin). We shall refer to these sections as the catalogue and the appendix. Where volume one was principally concerned with the Lycett Green gift of 1955, and volume two with acquisitions made since 1948, this volume includes most of those pictures acquired during the earlier years of the Gallery's history.

The present Art Gallery was built in 1879 as the Yorkshire Fine Art and Industrial Institution, with the proceeds from a great exhibition held in York in 1866. What we now see was only the preamble to a vast Main Hall used for miscellaneous social functions containing balconies and an organ. The building was administered by the officers of the Institution, who organised annual exhibitions. In 1882 John Burton (1799-1882), farmer, horse-dealer, mine owner and amateur artist, who lived at Poppleton Villa near York, was persuaded to bequeath to the Y.F.A.I.I. (as apart from the National Gallery in London) his collection of 129 paintings, then valued at £75,000. In this volume 85 of his pictures are catalogued and 27 appear in the appendix. Burton was not, in our sense of the word, a connoisseur, but he was rich and anxious to buy contemporary anecdotal pictures.

In 1892 York Corporation bought the Y.F.A.I.I., together with Burton's pictures, for £6,000. The City of York Corporation Art Galleries were first administered for the Council by a Technical Instruction and Higher Education Committee, since the York School of Art was allotted part of the premises. Annual art exhibitions continued until 1903, by which time public support had dwindled. The annual exhibitions had contained an average of over one thousand pictures; besides Burton's collection, old master loans (including, for a period, Lord Feversham's collection from Duncombe Park, and Lady Mary Thompson's from Sheriff Hutton Park), and contemporary paintings for sale were included. After 1903 more thematic exhibitions were arranged, such as *Old York Views and Worthies* in 1905, *William Etty* in 1911, *Paintings by the Moore Family* in 1912, and *York Artists* in 1913-14.

The Museums and Art Gallery Committee, instituted in 1912, placed the accent for an acquisitions policy on local history and topography and on local artists—whose willingness to donate their works seems, in retrospect, embarrassing. There was a modest purchase grant and the first oil painting to be bought was a view of Old Ouse Bridge by William Marlow, acquired for 15 guineas in 1902 (see vol. 2, p. 65); purchases were, however, few and far between, and then primarily of topographical, print-room material (such as Dr. W. A. Evelyn's collection in 1931). By 1939 the Gallery's collection of oil paintings comprised, besides the Burton collection, a very small number of dubious old masters, and a quantity of nineteenth- and twentieth-century paintings of, it must be admitted, an unprepossessing overall quality, nearly all connected by subject or artist with the City of York. From the pre-1939 period, besides the Burton pictures, this volume catalogues 3 purchases and 23 presentations, while the appendix contains 6 purchases and 95 presentations. What had started as healthy parochialism had, alas, become narrow-mindedness.

After the Second World War the parish pump was left behind, though not unattended. The advance was led by Mr. Hans Hess (Curator 1948-67), with the knowledgeable support of Eric Milner-White, Dean of York from 1941 until his death in 1963. An annual purchase grant made interesting purchases possible, such as the paintings by Courbet (1957), Rousseau (1958), Diaz (1963), and Isabey (1965); 49 are here catalogued. These also include the delightful Weedon Grossmith, the little Daubigny and a Frank Potter, perceptive rather than costly acquisitions. Meanwhile the Dean in this period presented the Gallery with 35 paintings of fine quality (as well as a large portion of his collection of twentieth-century stoneware) which placed the modern collection on an altogether new level; Sickert, Gilman, Steer, Conder and Gwen John, for example, were at last represented.

The catalogue describing all these paintings has been compiled by several hands, but the principal credit must go to Miss Norah Gillow, now at the William Morris Gallery. Valuable contributions were also made by Mr. David Rodgers and Mr. Hugh Brigstocke. They would all wish to acknowledge the help they received from London dealers (particularly Roland, Browse and Delbanco), Sotheby's, Christie's, the many individuals specified in catalogue entries, and from the Gallery files they inherited. This catalogue has been read and edited by me, and I hope justice has been done to that earlier research which is also gratefully recognised by the Art Gallery Committee.

JOHN INGAMELLS,
Curator.

December, 1973.

v

Dimensions	height precedes width
B.I.	British Institution, London
Burton Bequest, 1882	Bequeathed by John Burton (see Introduction)
c.	*circa*, about
C.A.S.	Contemporary Art Society
Dijon, 1957	Dijon, Musée des Beaux-Arts, *Peintures Anglaises des Collections d'York et du Yorkshire*, summer, 1957
Evelyn Collection, 1934	*Catalogue of the Evelyn and other Collections*, York, 1934; the oil paintings are numbered from 0.1. Local material only
Exh.:	exhibited at
Lit.:	literature (useful published references)
N.A.C.F.	National Art-Collections Fund
N.E.A.C.	New English Art Club, London
Preview	the quarterly bulletin published by York Art Gallery since January, 1948; continuous numbering and pagination
Prov.:	provenance
R.A.	Royal Academy, London
R.I.B.A.	Royal Institute of British Architects, London
R.S.A.	Royal Scottish Academy, Edinburgh
R.W.S.	Royal Society of Painters in Watercolours, London
Rawdon Bequest, 1895	Bequeathed by Dr. W. F. Rawdon of York, 1895
S.S.	Society of British Artists, Suffolk Street, London (1824-87)
York, 1856	York School of Art, Minster Yard, loan exhibition of pictures &c., 1856
York, 1866	York, Bootham Fields, *Yorkshire Fine Art and Industrial Exhibition*, 1866
York, 1879-1903	York Art Gallery buildings, annual exhibitions (see Introduction)
York Catalogue, 1907	*Catalogue of Pictures in the Permanent Collection*, compiled by E. Howarth, York, 1907
Y.F.A.I.I.	Yorkshire Fine Art and Industrial Institution

CATALOGUE

Norman ADAMS
1927 –

Painter of landscapes and religious subjects; born in London; has worked in London and Manchester.

882 Landscape

A brown landscape with black trees and dark sky.

Canvas 17½ x 23 *ins.,* 44.4 x 58.4 *cms.*

Signed and dated, lower left: *N. Adams. 56*

Lit.: *Preview,* 38, 1957, p. 375, illus.

Exh.: York, *Three Modern Artists,* 1956 (19).

Purchased from the artist, 1956.

892 Study in Ribblesdale

An undulating landscape with low horizon and white sky.

Canvas 20 x 30 *ins.,* 50.8 x 76.2 *cms.*

Signed and dated, lower left: *N. Adams. 56*

Exh.: York, *Three Modern Artists,* 1956 (4).

Presented by H. K. Henderson, 1957.

Jankel ADLER
1895 – 1949

Painter of figurative, imaginary subjects; born near Lodz, Poland; worked in Warsaw, Dusseldorf, Berlin, Paris, Scotland and London; died in Aldbourne, Wilts.

633 The Poet

Half-length figure seated at table with pen, paper, and hour glass, looking up at a bird, the symbol of inspiration, which flies overhead.

Canvas 44 x 34½ *ins.,* 112 x 87.7 *cms.*

Signed, lower left: *Adler,* inscribed and dated, verso: *(17) 1944*

Probably painted in London where Adler had settled in 1943.

Prov.: Executors of the artist, bought by the C.A.S., 1951.

Lit.: *Preview,* 20, 1952, pp. 224-25, illus.

Exh.: Brussels, *Jankel Adler,* 1946 (7); London, Arts Council, *Recent Purchases of the C.A.S.,* 1951 (2), and *Jankel Adler,* 1951 (24); Dijon, 1957 (43).

Presented by the Contemporary Art Society, 1952.   [*Plate 44*]

Richard ANSDELL
1815 – 1885

Animal painter; born in Liverpool; worked in London, travelled in Spain; died in Farnborough.

280   Feeding the Calves

A woman with a dog watching two calves feeding from a trough by her feet.

Canvas 30 x 25 *ins.*, 76.2 x 63.5 *cms.*

Signed and dated, lower right: *R. Ansdell 1860*

Ansdell exhibited another painting with this title at the R.A., 1855, no.343.

Lit.:   *York Catalogue,* 1907, no. 48.
Burton Bequest, 1882.

337   Drovers in Glen Sligichan, Isle of Skye

In a hilly landscape a shepherd and his dog round up sheep by a foreground stream; to the right a boy, followed by a woman carrying bales of straw, leads a white horse.

Canvas 39½ x 84 *ins.*, 100.3 x 213.4 *cms.*

Signed and dated, lower right: *R. Ansdell 1860*

The figures were painted by W. P. Frith (q.v.). The picture was sadly overcleaned in 1906 when a flock of sheep 'disappeared'.

Lit.:   *York Catalogue,* 1907, no. 103.
Burton Bequest, 1882.

John ARMSTRONG
1893 – 1973

Painter of decorative subjects; born in Hastings; worked in London.

1038   Funeral of a Poet

A chariot containing branches and an urn drawn by four plumed horses.

Tempera on plywood 19 x 30 *ins.*, 48.3 x 76.2 *cms.*

Signed and dated, lower right: *JA '37*

Prov.:   Lefevre Gallery, 1938, bought Milner-White.
Lit.:   *The Studio,* 117, April, 1939, p. 142, illus.
Exh.:   London, Lefevre Gallery, *John Armstrong,* 1938 (21).
Presented by the Very Rev. E. Milner-White, 1963.

1039 Goatherd.

A robed figure in profile with a staff and five goats.

Tempera on plywood 21¾ x 29½ *ins., 55.2 x 75 cms.*

Signed and dated, lower right: *JA '37*

Prov.: Lefevre Gallery, 1938, bought Milner-White.

Exh.: London, Lefevre Gallery, *John Armstrong,* 1938 (35).

Presented by the Very Rev. E. Milner-White, 1963.

John BANTING
1902 – 1972

Painter of decorative subjects; born in Chelsea; worked in London and Paris; died in Hastings.

38 Composition

Still life with classical head, fish and mussels.

Panel 16 x 22 *ins., 41.2 x 55.8 cms.*

Inscribed in pencil, verso: *Banting*

Painted c.1930.

Prov.: Bought by the C.A.S., 1934, as *Design.*

Presented by the Contemporary Art Society, 1949.

Émile BARAU
1851 – 1931

Landscape painter; born in Rheims; worked in Denmark, Holland and France; died in Neuilly-sur-Seine.

438 The Village Church

A white-washed cruciform church with tower at the junction of two lanes.

Panel 16¼ x 21½ *ins., 41.3 x 54.6 cms.*

Signed (and originally dated?), lower right: *Emile Barau*

Possibly painted c.1885.

Prov.: A. Coulter, York.

Lit.: *Preview,* 12, 1950, p. 141, illus.

Purchased, 1950.

652 Landscape with woman washing

A summer landscape with a woman washing clothes in a foreground stream.

Canvas 28¾ x 32½ *ins., 73.6 x 82.6 cms.*

Signed and dated, lower right: *Emile Barau 1887*
PROV.:   Anon. sale, Christie's, 10th June, 1921 (150), bought Briggs; A. Coulter, York.
LIT.:   *Preview, 21, 1953, p. 131, illus.*
Presented by Mr. and Mrs. Sykes Rymer through the York Civic Trust, 1952.

ALFRED WALTER BAYES
1832 – 1909

Painter of domestic genre; worked in London.

62   Day Dreams
A girl in a white dress, looking right, reclining on a couch.
Canvas 20 x 27 ins., 50.8 x 68.6 cms.
Signed, lower left: *A. W. Bayes*
Painted c.1902.
PROV.:   Bought by the C.A.S. before 1913.
EXH.:   R.A., 1903 (650); London, Goupil Gallery, April, 1913 (150), lent by the C.A.S.
Presented by the Contemporary Art Society, 1923.

ANTHONY BENJAMIN
1931 –

Born in Boarhunt, Hampshire; has worked in Paris, London and Canada.

1154   Painting No. 1
Dark abstract shapes on a red background.
Canvas 74½ x 93 ins., 188.6 x 236.2 cms.
Signed and dated, verso: *Anthony Benjamin/Sept 65/March 66*
Presented by the Contemporary Art Society, 1968.

OLIVER BEVAN
1941 –

Born in Peterborough; has worked in London and Farnham.

1122   Flickering Grid II
Grid pattern in dark grey and white.
Emulsion on hardboard 48 x 36 ins., 122 x 92 cms.
Painted in 1965.
LIT.:   *Preview, 74, 1966, pp. 689-92, illus.*
Presented by the Friends of York Art Gallery, 1966.

Pierre-Marie BEYLE
1838 – 1902

Genre painter; born in Lyons; worked in Paris and Normandy, travelled in Algeria.

314 The Gossips

Three women in peasant costume, one seated and two kneeling, cleaning brass vessels in a garden.

Canvas 52½ x 77 *ins.*, 133.4 x 195.6 *cms.*

Lit.: *York Catalogue*, 1907, no. 95.

Exh.: London, Continental Gallery, March, 1879 (29), as *Gossip.*

Burton Bequest, 1882.

Roger BISSIÈRE
1888 – 1964

Painter of portraits, still life and abstract subjects; born in Villeréal; worked in Bordeaux and Paris.

463 Still life with Glass and Grapes

A glass, apple, grapes and knife on a napkin.

Canvas 14¾ x 21½ *ins.*, 37.5 x 54.6 *cms.*

Signed, lower right: *Bissière*

Painted c.1920, in emulation of Braque.

Prov.: Lord Duveen, presented to the C.A.S., 1928.

Lit.: *Preview*, 9, 1950, p. 104, illus.

Exh.: London, Arts Council, *Recent Acquisitions of the C.A.S.,* 1949 (8).

Presented by the Contemporary Art Society, 1949.

879 Woman in a Straw Hat

A seated woman in a straw hat, resting her head on her hand.

Canvas 21¾ x 20 *ins.*, 55.3 x 50.8 *cms.*

Painted with a loose impressionist technique which suggests a date of c.1915-20.

Prov.: Swiss private collection; Roland, Browse and Delbanco, 1956.

Lit.: *Preview*, 37, 1957, p. 367, illus. cover.

Purchased, 1956.

Jacques-Émile BLANCHE
1861 – 1942

Painter of portraits and urban life; born in Paris; worked in Paris and London; died in Paris.

26   Sloane Street, London

Sloane Street, with Sloane Square in the background; crowded pavements and horse-drawn omnibuses.

Millboard 33 x 39 *ins.*, 83.9 x 99 *cms.*

Signed, lower right: *J. E. Blanche*

One of a series of views of well-known London streets which the artist painted c.1908-09. Another, *Ludgate Hill,* is in the Tate Gallery (5755), and a third is described below, no.566.

PROV.:   The artist; presented by the artist's brother, Georges A. Melvil-Blanche, to the C.A.S., 1947.

LIT.:   J. E. Blanche, *Portraits of a Lifetime,* 1937, illus. f.p. 245, as in the collection of the artist; *Preview,* 5, 1949, p. 49, illus.

Presented by the Contemporary Art Society, 1948.

566   Piccadilly Circus

Piccadilly Circus with horse-drawn vehicles and pedestrians.

Canvas 27½ x 37 *ins.*, 69.9 x 94 *cms.*

Signed, lower right: *J. E. Blanche*

Painted c.1908-09, see no.26 above.

PROV.:   Roland, Browse and Delbanco.

Presented by the Friends of York Art Gallery, 1951.

David BOMBERG
1890 – 1957

Painter of figurative and abstract subjects; born in Birmingham; worked in London, travelled in Europe and the Mediterranean; died in London.

941   Man's Head

Head and shoulders of a dark-haired, sallow man, facing right.

Canvas 20 x 16 *ins.*, 50.8 x 40.6 *cms.*

Signed and dated, lower right: *Bomberg 37*

One of a series of self-portraits executed c.1937. A related portrait was exhibited at the Tate Gallery, *Bomberg,* 1967, no.70, and a stylistically similar portrait of the artist's wife, also of 1937, was exhibited at the Bomberg memorial exhibition, London, 1958, no.35.

PROV.: The artist; A. A. Stambois, London.

LIT.: *Preview*, 47/48, 1959, pp. 446-47, illus.

Purchased, 1959. [*Plate 39*]

1055 The Bath

Four nude yellow figures with a baby gathered round a tin bath within a draped interior.

Canvas 20 x 24 *ins., 50.8 x 61 cms.*

Signed and dated, lower right: *Bomberg '22*

A more resolved version of a watercolour *Magdalenian Theme* painted in 1920, in the collection of Mrs. Lilian Bomberg. According to Mrs. Bomberg (letter in Gallery files dated 29th April, 1967), 'The subjects for the composition and around this same theme do appear in the 1919 wash drawings and in the Imaginative Compositions oil on paper of 1920, one of which is entitled *Tent Family...*'

PROV.: Dr. Sidney Schiff, presented to the C.A.S., 1926.

LIT.: *Preview*, 64, 1963, illus. cover.

EXH.: Venice, *XVI International Exhibition*, 1928 (66), lent by the C.A.S.; London, Whitechapel Art Gallery, May, 1931 (31).

Presented by the Contemporary Art Society, 1963. [*Plate 41*]

FRANÇOIS BONVIN
1817 – 1887

Painter of still life; born and worked in Paris; died in St. Germain-en-Laye.

616 Still life

A laden pewter plate, a spoon and a drinking glass on a table covered by a white cloth.

Canvas 15¾ x 11½ *ins., 40 x 29.2 cms.*

Signed and dated, upper left: *F. Bonvin, 1879.*

PROV.: G. Tempelaere, Paris; Marlborough Gallery, bought Milner-White.

LIT.: *Preview*, 18, 1952, p. 208, illus. cover.

EXH.: London, Marlborough Gallery, November, 1951 (3).

Presented by the Very Rev. E. Milner-White, 1952. [*Plate 16*]

SAMUEL BOUGH
1822 – 1878

Landscape painter; born in Carlisle; worked in Manchester, Glasgow and Edinburgh.

294   Entrance to Cadzow Forest, near Glasgow
A wooded country lane with a cottage, left.
Canvas 26 x 36 *ins., 66 x 91.4 cms.*
Signed and dated, lower left: *Sam Bough 1859*
Lit.:   *York Catalogue*, 1907, no. 118, illus. p. 45.
Burton Bequest, 1882.

Émile BOUNEAU
1902 –

Born in Avignon; worked in Paris.

1033   Boy in a red shirt
A small boy in a red shirt lying on a bed, facing right.
Millboard 25½ x 21¼ *ins., 64.8 x 54 cms.*
Signed, lower left: *E. Bouneau*
Prov.:   The artist, 1939, bought Milner-White.
Lit.:   *Preview,* 63, 1963, illus. cover.
Exh.:   Cambridge, April, 1939.
Presented by the Very Rev. E. Milner-White, 1963.

Henry BRIGHT
c.1810 – 1873

Landscape painter; born in Saxmundham, Suffolk; worked in Norwich, London and Ipswich; died in Ipswich.

132   An old Welsh Watermill
A watermill on a rocky hillside, beneath a showery sky.
Canvas 24¼ x 43 *ins., 61.6 x 109.2 cms.*
Signed and dated, lower right: *H. Bright 1860*
A related oil study for the picture was sold at Sotheby's, 11th November, 1970, lot 3.   A pencil sketch, signed and dated 1859, was with Folio Fine Art, London, in 1970.
Lit.:   *York Catalogue*, 1907, no. 42.
Burton Bequest, 1882.

236   Landscape
A rocky pool with a clump of trees, left, and an open landscape, right.
Canvas 18 x 24 *ins., 45.7 x 60.9 cms.*
Signed and dated, lower right: *H. Bright 1860*
Lit.:   *York Catalogue*, 1907, no. 23.
Burton Bequest, 1882.

242 Scene in the English Lakes—Derwentwater

Derwentwater surrounded by hills, with a rocky foreground and a single figure, right.

Canvas 10 x 18 *ins., 25.4 x 45.7 cms.*

Signed and dated, lower left: *H. Bright 1866*

LIT.: *York Catalogue,* 1907, no. 69.
Burton Bequest, 1882.

267 The Cottage Door

A young woman standing knitting by an open cottage door with a small dog at her feet.

Canvas 28 x 23 *ins., 71.1 x 58.4 cms.*

Signed and dated, centre right: *J. J. Hill 1864/H. Bright*

The figure and dog were presumably painted by Hill (q.v.) who collaborated with Bright on this picture.

PROV.: John Gooch of Norwood sale, Christie's, 12th May, 1876 (59), bought Parker.
LIT.: *York Catalogue,* 1907, no. 47.
EXH.: Norwich, *Henry Bright,* 1973 (13).
Burton Bequest, 1882.

340 Feeding the Pets

A girl before a thatched cottage feeding corn to fowl; a hilly landscape and a stream with a waterfall to the left.

Canvas 40 x 50 *ins., 101.6 x 127 cms.*

Signed and dated, lower right: *H. Bright 1858/ I. Henzell*

The genre scene of the girl feeding the fowl was presumably painted by Henzell (q.v.) who collaborated with Bright on this picture.

LIT.: *The Art Journal,* 1860, p. 299; *York Catalogue,* 1907, no. 56.
EXH.: London, Hayward and Leggatt, 1860.
Burton Bequest, 1882.

GUSTAVE BRION
active 1847 – 1868

Born in Rothau in the Vosges; worked in Paris.

300 The Cattle Tenter

A man, a boy and a dog walking in front of a herd of cattle, beneath an evening sky.

Canvas $31\frac{3}{4}$ x $25\frac{1}{2}$ *ins., 80.6 x 64.8 cms.*

Signed and dated, lower left: *G Brion 1857*

PROV.: (possibly) George Taylor sale, Christie's, 14th May, 1860 (218), as *Returning from the Pastures;* Burton.
LIT.: *York Catalogue,* 1907, no. 91.
Burton Bequest, 1882.

John BURR
1831 – 1893

Domestic genre painter; born in Edinburgh; worked in Edinburgh and London.

197   What ails it, Grandad?

An old man examining a clock, watched by a child and a lady.

Canvas 26¼ x 37 *ins., 66.6 x 93.9 cms.*

Signed and dated, lower left: *John Burr 1872*

LIT.:   *York Catalogue,* 1907, no. 116.

EXH.:   York, 1880 (570), lent Burton; Glasgow, 1911 (57).

Burton Bequest, 1882.

John CALLOW
1822 – 1878

Marine painter; born in Greenwich; worked in Paris and London.

196   A Fresh Breeze

In a rough sea a fishing boat, centre, a two-master, left, and other shipping beyond.

Canvas 24 x 42 *ins., 61 x 106.7 cms.*

Signed and dated, lower right: *Callow 1867*(?), and initialled *JC* on sails of the foremost boat.

LIT.:   *York Catalogue,* 1907, no. 46.

EXH.:   York, 1880 (976), lent Burton (for sale at 15 gns.).

Burton Bequest, 1882.

Valerios CALOUTSIS
1927 –

Born in Crete; has worked in London and Paris.

1009   Forme Aride

Black gesso in low relief incised with straight lines picked out in silver.

Gesso and metallic paint on canvas 49 x 38 *ins., 125 x 96.6 cms.*

Signed and dated, lower centre: *V. Caloutsis 62*

PROV.:   Redfern Gallery.

LIT.:   *The Studio,* 164, July, 1962, pp. 12-17, illus.; *Preview,* 59, 1962, pp. 558-59, illus.

EXH.:   London, Redfern Gallery, May, 1962 (1).

Purchased, 1962.

Z. CARABIN
active 1880 – 1890

308 The Public Letter Writer

A man in a brown cap and gown writing a letter for a woman who stands with her companion before his desk.

Canvas 31 x 38 *ins., 78.7 x 96.5 cms.*

Signed and dated, lower right: *Z Carabin 1880*

Lit.: *York Catalogue,* 1907, no. 90.
Burton Bequest, 1882.

John Wilson CARMICHAEL
1800 – 1868

Marine painter; born in Newcastle; worked in Newcastle and London, travelled in Holland, Italy, the Baltic and the Crimea; died in Scarborough.

290 Robin Hood's Bay, Yorkshire

Two boats and figures on a sand bar, right, with other boats and figures beyond; houses and cliffs behind.

Canvas 28 x 36 *ins., 71.1 x 91.5 cms.*

Signed and dated, lower right: *J W Carmichael 1856.*

Bequeathed by Mrs. Hannah Deighton, 1913.

311 Whale-fishing in a Polar sea

A whale pursued by a whaler in a rough sea among icebergs.

Canvas 34 x 48 *ins., 86.5 x 122 cms.*

Signed and dated, lower right: *J W Carmichael 1845*

Lit.: *Preview,* 71, 1965, p. 669, illus.
Presented by the Trustees of the De Grey Rooms, York, 1913.

363 An Engagement between the 'Nymphe' and the 'Cleopatra'

On a choppy sea a three-masted French vessel, the Cleopatra, having lost one of her masts, is about to be overpowered by the English vessel the Nymphe, who fires at her from the right; a Frenchman clings to an upturned life-boat in the foreground.

Canvas 30 x 42 *ins., 76.2 x 106.7 cms.*

Inscribed, verso, on the stretcher: *the Nymphe & Cleopatra The first engagement in the War Painted by J W Carmichael*

In poor condition; the canvas has been torn and awaits relining.

The action took place in the Channel on 18th June, 1793, and resulted in the capture of the French 40-gun frigate by the Nymphe, a 36-gun frigate commanded by Captain Edward Pellew (information supplied by Edward Archibald of the National Maritime Museum).

No. 363 is based on a painting by Nicholas Pocock (engraved by Medland for the *Naval Chronicle*, vol. 2, 1799, p. 237, and possibly exhibited at the R.A. in 1795, no.23). Mr. Archibald points out that the French ensign in no.363 is of a post-1794 pattern, an error avoided in Pocock's original painting.
Acquired before 1948.

386   Queen Victoria's arrival in Edinburgh

The royal vessel, the Royal George, seen in evening light surrounded by other small craft, their crews holding burning torches.

Canvas 28 x 46 *ins.*, 71.1 x 116.8 *cms.*

Queen Victoria arrived at Edinburgh on 3rd September, 1842. Carmichael exhibited two related drawings, *The Royal Yacht off Edinburgh* and *The Arrival of the Royal Squadron* at the R.A. in 1843.
LIT.:   *York Catalogue of Oil Paintings*, vol. 2, 1963, p. 9.
Presented by the Trustees of the De Grey Rooms, York, 1913.

1012   Ships beating off a lee shore

Rocky coastline with a ruined castle, right, and a sailing vessel in a rough sea, left.

Canvas 17 x 24¾ *ins.*, 43.2 x 62.9 *cms.*

Signed and dated, lower right: *J. W. Carmichael 1845*

Possibly identifiable with the picture exhibited at the R.A. in 1849, no.296, as *Heavy Weather: riding on a Lee Shore.*
PROV.:   H. J. Ware, by descent.
EXH.:   York, 1879 (1134), lent H. J. Ware.
Presented by Col. N. Innes Ware, 1962.

EUGÈNE CARRIÈRE
1849 – 1906

Painter of family life; born in Gournay (Seine-et-Marne); worked in Paris, travelled in London; died in Paris.

957   Head of a Woman

Head and shoulders of a young woman painted in greys and browns.
Canvas 18 x 15 *ins.*, 45.8 x 38.1 *cms.*
Signed, lower right: *Eugène Carrière*
Probably painted c.1890.

PROV.: Louis Le Sidaner; Dr. Charpentier sale, Galerie Charpentier, Paris, 30th March, 1954 (83); Roland, Browse and Delbanco.
LIT.: *Preview*, 50, 1960, p. 476, illus. cover.
Purchased, 1960.

LEOPOLD DE CAUWER
active second half of 19th century

Worked in Furstenwalde, near Berlin; exhibited in Berlin and Dresden.

301 Cattle

Two cows in a marshy field with a flock of sheep and a shepherd.

Canvas 23 x 32 *ins., 58.4 x 81.3 cms.*

Signed and dated, lower left: *Leop, de Cauwer fc/56*

LIT.: *York Catalogue*, 1907, no. 34.
Burton Bequest, 1882.

LOUIS JOSEPH CAYMANS
1826 – 1877

Painter of domestic genre; born in Brussels; worked in Belgium; died in Ixelles.

129 The Bird Cage

Two women seated at table, one of whom offers a caged bird a crumb.

Panel 15⅛ x 11½ *ins., 38.5 x 29.2 cms.*

Signed and dated, lower right: *Louis Caymans 1865*

LIT.: *York Catalogue*, 1907, no. 71.
Burton Bequest, 1882.

MARIE CAZIN (NÉE GUILLET)
1844 – 1924

Landscape painter; born at Paimboeuf (Loire Inférieure); worked in France; died in Éguilen (Pas de Calais).

462 Landscape: Village among trees

A field of green corn with a figure, right; roof tops among the trees beyond.

Canvas 9¾ x 13½ *ins., 24.8 x 34.3 cms.*

PROV.: Beaux Arts Gallery, 1950.
Purchased, 1950.

980   A Lane

A bend in a lane running between wooded fields with a man and two women carrying hay and rakes walking into the distance, right.

Millboard 8¾ x 11¾ *ins., 22.2 x 29.8 cms.*

Signed, lower right: *M C*

PROV.: Miss E. W. Browne, sold Christie's, 20th October, 1960 (124), bought Agnew.
LIT.:   *Preview,* 55, 1961, p. 528, illus.
Purchased, 1961.

EDWARD JOHN COBBETT
1815 – 1899

Landscape painter; born in London; worked in London, Wales and Brittany.

199   A Welsh Interior

A cottage interior with two girls seated near a window teasing out wool for spinning, while a third looks on.

Millboard 16½ x 20½ *ins., 41.9 x 52.1 cms.*

Signed and dated, lower left: *E J Cobbett 1856*

LIT.:   *The Art Journal,* 1856, p. 163; *York Catalogue,* 1907, no. 22; C. Wood,
         Dictionary of Victorian Painters, 1971, p. 27.
EXH.:   R.A., 1856 (69); S.S., 1860 (191).
Burton Bequest, 1882.

CHARLES COLLINS
active 1867 – 1903

Landscape painter; worked at Dorking, Surrey.

142   Showery weather

Beneath a threatening sky, an open landscape with a thatched shed and sheltering cattle, left.

Canvas 16 x 26 *ins., 40.6 x 66 cms.*

Signed and dated, lower right: *Charles Collins 1875* and signed, inscribed and dated verso: *(No. 1) Showery Weather Charles Collins—1875—*

LIT.:   *York Catalogue,* 1907, no. 75.
EXH.:   S.S., 1875-76 (293).
Burton Bequest, 1882.

CHARLES CONDER
1868 – 1909

Landscape and decorative painter; born in London; worked in Australia, Paris and London; travelled in Algiers; died in Virginia Water.

1030 Yport

Beneath a summer sky, white cliffs and sea with a boy dressing in the foreground; Yport is on the coast of Normandy between Fécamp and Étretat.

Canvas 19¼ x 23½ *ins., 48.9 x 59.7 cms.*

Signed, dated and inscribed, lower right: *Yport/Charles Conder 1892.*

Possibly identifiable with a painting *Cliffs at Yport* mentioned by F. Gibson in 1914 (*Conder, His Life and Work*, pp. 34, 94), as being dated 1891.

PROV.: Mrs. Mitchell; O. Oppenheimer; Milner-White.

LIT.: *Preview*, 63, 1963, p. 602, illus.

EXH.: London, Tate Gallery, *Conder*, 1927 (84), lent Oppenheimer; Sheffield, *Conder*, 1967 (19); R.A., 1974 (124).

Presented by the Very Rev. E. Milner-White, 1963. [*Plate 27*]

PIERRE OLIVIER JOSEPH COOMANS
1816 – 1889

Genre painter; born in Brussels; worked in Ghent, Antwerp and France; travelled in the Mediterranean; died in Boulogne-sur-Seine.

288 The Mask

A scene from Roman antiquity; a boy frightens a baby with a grimacing mask, while their mother winds thread with a serving girl.

Panel 20¾ x 27½ *ins., 52.7 x 69.9 cms.*

Signed and dated, lower right: *Joseph Coomans. 1870.*

PROV.: Joseph Craven sale, Christie's, 30th March, 1874 (61), as *A Pompeian Interior*.

Burton Bequest, 1882.

THOMAS SIDNEY COOPER
1803 – 1902

Animal painter; born in Canterbury; worked in London and Brussels; died in Canterbury.

315 Canterbury Meadows

Cattle and sheep in a sunlit wooded meadow; two women and soldiers, centre, picnicking; Canterbury cathedral in the far distance.

Canvas 58 x 94 *ins., 127.3 x 238.8 cms.*

Signed and dated, lower right: *T. Sidney Cooper A.R.A./1858*

A painting of this title belonging to F. A. Millbank was exhibited at York in 1880, no. 52, and may possibly have then been bought by Burton.

LIT.: *York Catalogue*, 1907, no. 44.

Burton Bequest, 1882.

497 Landscape with cattle and sheep

Open downland with sheep, foreground left, and three cows, right, cliffs and sea behind.

Panel 20 x 24 *ins.*, 50.8 x 61 *cms.*

Signed and dated, lower left: *T. Sidney Cooper RA 1875*

Bequeathed by Miss M. M. Robinson, 1950.

GUSTAVE COURBET
1819 – 1877

Painter of landscapes and urban life; born in Ornans; worked in Paris and Switzerland, travelled in Germany; died in La Tour de Peilz, Switzerland.

893 Swiss Landscape

To the left, a rocky foreshore with a small cliff overgrown with trees; to the right, a lake with distant snow-capped mountains.

Millboard 13½ x 18½ *ins.*, 34.3 x 47 *cms.*

Signed and dated, lower left: *69/G. Courbet.*

Probably one of the paintings made in October 1869 on Courbet's return to Ornans, by way of Switzerland, from Munich (where he had received the Cross of the Order of Merit of St. Michael).

PROV.: Alexandre Bernheim-Jeune sale, Paris, 15th May, 1917 (11), bought Durand-Ruel and Bernheim-Jeune; 26th July, 1919, bought Mohammed Mahmoud; Jacques Dubourg, Paris; Roland, Browse and Delbanco.
LIT.: *Preview*, 39, 1957, pp. 382-83, illus.
EXH.: London, Roland, Browse and Delbanco, June, 1956 (16).
Purchased, 1957   [*Plate 11*]

RICHARD DADD
1819 – 1886

Landscape and visionary painter; born in Chatham, Kent; worked in London, travelled in the Mediterranean; committed as insane, 1844, to Bethlem Hospital and Broadmoor; died in Broadmoor.

221 Landscape

A rustic cottage in fields, with a stream in the foreground and a distant spire; a figure in blue stands by a fence on the right.

Panel 6½ x 10¼ *ins.*, 16.5 x 26 *cms.*

Signed and dated, lower left: *R Dad ...37*

Dadd entered the R.A. schools in 1837 and this landscape is an orthodox academic sketch. The scene has been tentatively identified by J. B. L. Allen as Bickley Vale in Devon, since Dadd exhibited a landscape of that title at the B.I. in 1838, no. 57. Greysmith supposes a West country subject and suggests it may have been painted *en plein air*. Another painting which appears to show the same locale, entitled *The Bridge* (panel 8¼ x 11¼ ins., dated 1837), was sold at Sotheby's, 3rd June, 1964, lot 91. (Greysmith, pl. 15).

PROV.: Mrs. Grace; sold Sotheby's, 24th November, 1948 (40).

LIT.: J. B. L. Allen, 'Mad Robin: Richard Dadd', *The Art Quarterly*, 1967, p. 19, fig. 10; D. Greysmith, *Richard Dadd*, 1973, pp. 75, 167, fig. 14.

EXH.: London, Tate Gallery, *Richard Dadd*, 1974 (9).

Purchased, with a donation from Sir Ivo Thomson, 1948.

CHARLES-FRANÇOIS DAUBIGNY
1817 – 1878

Landscape painter; born in Paris; worked in Paris, travelled in England and Italy; died in Paris.

461 The Waterfall

A wooded rocky landscape with river and waterfall.

Panel 7 x 11¼ ins., 17.8 x 28.6 cms.

Stamped in red, lower right: *Vente Daubigny*

Robert L. Herbert (letter in Gallery files dated 20th December, 1967) suggests a date of c.1870-75. The only picture in the Daubigny sale which would seem to fit the York panel was lot 52, *Chute d'eau dans le Dauphiné*, 18.5 x 26.5 cms., but this was then described as having been painted in 1853 —either in error or because it was another picture.

PROV.: (possibly) Daubigny sale, Paris 6-11th May, 1878 (52); Countess Manvers, Keighley, Yorkshire; A. Coulter, York.

LIT.: *Preview*, 12, 1950, p. 135, illus.

Purchased, 1950.   [*Plate 11*]

HENRY DAWSON
1811 – 1878

Landscape painter; born in Hull; worked in Nottingham, Liverpool and London; died in Chiswick.

193 Landscape

A boy walking down a path; a stone bridge and a birch tree to the left, and a flat open landscape with cattle and some cottages to the right.

Canvas 19¾ x 30 ins., 50.2 x 76.2 cms.

Signed and dated, lower right: *H Dawson 1855*
LIT.:   *York Catalogue,* 1907, no. 109.
Burton Bequest, 1882.

252 The Cliffs of Dover

Three figures on the beach, centre, near a hut, with the cliffs behind them.
Canvas 18½ x 24½ *ins.,* 47 x 62.2 *cms.*
Signed and dated, lower left: *H D* (monogram) *1850*
LIT.:   *York Catalogue,* 1907, no. 25.
Burton Bequest, 1882.

272 Landscape in Derbyshire

Cattle drinking at a pool tended by a woman on a white horse; a rocky
cliff to the left, a broad wooded valley to the right.
Panel 27½ x 37 *ins.,* 69.9 x 94 *cms.*
Signed and dated, lower right: *H Dawson 1851*
LIT.:   *York Catalogue,* 1907, no. 45; *Preview,* 44, 1958, p. 426, illus.
EXH.:   Dijon, 1957 (30).
Burton Bequest, 1882.

HENRY THOMAS DAWSON
active 1860 – 1878

Landscape and marine painter; son of Henry Dawson (q.v.); worked in
London.

385 Port Madoc, North Wales

The harbour at low tide, with two sailing boats, centre, and a steam tug
moored at a quay, left; other sailing boats and a paddle steamer are moored
at the quays, right, before a tree-covered hill crowned with a flag pole.
Canvas 28 x 42 *ins.,* 71.1 x 106.7 *cms.*
Signed and dated, lower right: *18. HTD* (monogram) *Jan^r 74*
In poor condition; several paint losses.
LIT.:   *York Catalogue,* 1907, no. 26.
EXH.:   S.S., 1874 (91).
Burton Bequest, 1882.

NARCISSE-VIRGILIO DIAZ DE LA PEÑA
1806 – 1876

Landscape and genre painter; born in Bordeaux; worked in Paris and
Fontainebleau; died at Menton.

1059　The Forest of Fontainebleau

A woodland glade with a pool.

Panel 12 x 17¼ *ins., 30.5 x 43.8 cms.*

Signed, lower left: *N. Diaz.* and stamped in red, lower right: *Vente Diaz.*

Probably painted c.1865-70.

PROV.:　Third Diaz sale, Paris, 22-27th January, 1877; Goupil, Paris; ? M. H. Schweitz, New York; H. K. Thaw, New York; Roland, Browse and Delbanco.

LIT.:　*Preview,* 65, 1964, pp. 618-19, illus.

Purchased with the aid of a grant from the Victoria and Albert Museum, 1963.

[Plate 10]

1214　Woman washing by a stream

In a rocky landscape with distant trees and hills, a woman washing clothes in a stream.

Panel 12½ x 15¾ *ins., 31.5 x 40.5 cms.*

Signed, lower left: *N. Diaz.*

Another version, in which part of the wood at the right hand side is excluded and a seated woman bathing replaces the woman washing, is in the Victoria and Albert Museum, (Ionides Collection, no.61, panel 9½ x 12⅞ ins.).

PROV.:　Aubry, Paris; Roland, Browse and Delbanco; Viscount Radcliffe; Sotheby's, 8th July, 1971 (10), withdrawn; N.A.C.F.

EXH.:　London, Roland, Browse and Delbanco, April, 1958 (23).

Presented by the Viscount Radcliffe through the National Art-Collection Fund, 1971.

PETER LEONARD DONNELLY
1935 –

Born in London; has worked in London.

1121　Red Plot

Simple abstract red and black composition.

Hardboard 48 x 68 *ins., 122 x 172.5 cms.*

Painted in 1966.

LIT.:　*Preview,* 74, 1966, pp. 689-92, illus.

Presented by the Friends of York Art Gallery, 1966.

CHARLES DUKES
active 1825 – 1865

Painter of domestic genre; worked in London.

254 The Bird's Nest

By a hedge, a mother rests with a baby to whom the father shows a bird's nest.

Canvas 24 x 20 *ins.,* 61 x 50.8 *cms.*

Signed, lower right: *Charles Dukes*

PROV.:   Henry Wallis sale, Christie's, 16th November, 1860 (23), bought Skelton; Burton.

LIT.:   *The Art Journal,* 1859, p. 80; *York Catalogue,* 1907, no. 24; *Preview,* 90, 1970, p. 823, illus.; C. Wood, *Dictionary of Victorian Painters,* 1971, pp. 41, 256, illus.

EXH.:   B.I., 1859 (7).

Burton Bequest, 1882.

RONALD OSSORY DUNLOP
1894 – 1973

Figurative painter; born in Dublin; worked in Manchester, Wimbledon, Paris and Sussex.

63 Still life

Bottles and a vase of flowers on a table; a window to the right.

Canvas 22 x 25 *ins.,* 55.9 x 63.5 *cms.*

Signed, lower right: *Dunlop*

Painted in or before 1929.

PROV.:   Redfern Gallery, 1929, bought by the C.A.S.

EXH.:   London, Whitechapel Gallery, *C.A.S. Paintings and Drawings,* 1931 (70), as *Still Life at a window*; (possibly, Tate Gallery, *Empire Art Loan Collections Fund,* 1935 (65).

Presented by the Contemporary Art Society, 1935.

JULES DUPRÉ
1811 – 1889

Landscape painter; born near Nantes; worked in Paris, south west France and at L'Isle-Adam where he died.

24 Landscape

A pool in the foreground with two cows and a moored boat; a cottage with figure in the right middle distance; trees and open fields beyond.

Panel 15½ x 25½ *ins.,* 39.4 x 64.8 *cms.*

Signed, lower right: *Dupre*

PROV.:   A. Coulter, York.

LIT.:   *Preview,* 4, 1948, pp. 4-5.

Presented by J. S. Gans, 1948.

Joseph Laurens DYCKMANS
1811 – 1888

Painter of domestic genre; born in Lierre, Belgium; worked and died in Antwerp.

310 The Lady of Fashion

An interior; a young woman stands holding a silk shawl round her shoulders and looking left to where a young man sits on a sofa with a spaniel jumping up at his knee; in the centre, a table on which materials are displayed, and a woman in a bonnet conversing with a man who inspects bills.

Canvas 32½ x 29½ *ins., 82.6 x 74.9 cms.*

Signed and dated, lower right: *J. Dyckmans. 1854*

A 19th-century label, verso, gives the alternative title, *The Coquette.*

PROV.: Everard & Co., London, sold Southgate & Co., July, 1870, bought Hastings.

LIT.: *York Catalogue*, 1907, no. 96.

Burton Bequest, 1882.

Henry H. EMMERSON
1831 – 1895

Genre painter; born in Chester-le-Street, Co. Durham; worked in Newcastle, died at Cullercoats.

167 The Critiques

Two women standing by a rustic fence in a field bordered by wild flowers.

Canvas 20½ x 18½ *ins., 52.1 x 47 cms.,* feigned oval

Signed and dated, lower left: *H H. Emmerson 1863.,* and inscribed with title, verso.

LIT.: *York Catalogue*, 1907, no. 73; C. Wood, *Dictionary of Victorian Painters,* 1971, p. 44.

Burton Bequest, 1882.

John FAED
1820 – 1902

Genre and narrative painter; born in Burley Mill, Kirkcudbrightshire, eldest brother of Thomas (q.v.) and James Faed; worked in Galloway, Edinburgh, London and Ardmore in Scotland; died at Burley Mill.

1190   The Thirsty Customer

A busy London street scene, with a man in a tartan cap offering more water to a little boy who is drinking from a tin cup; beyond them a girl is asking directions from a woman and two errand boys.

Canvas 53 x 44½ *ins.*, 134.6 x 113 *cms.*

Signed, centre right: *J. Faed*

An inscription on the delivery van (in the background, right) identifies the firm as the Wenham Lake Ice Co. who operated from premises at 164a The Strand—the address on the van—from 1846-59. Faed was working in London between 1862 and 1880 and he exhibited at the R.A. between 1855 and 1893.

PROV.: Art Collectors' Association, sold Christie's, 21st December, 1923 (72), bought Wolff; Spink & Sons; English private collection.

Presented Anonymously, 1970.   [*Plate 3*]

THOMAS FAED
1826 – 1900

Genre and narrative painter; born in Burley Mill, Kirkcudbrightshire, brother of John (q.v.); worked in Edinburgh and London, where he died.

147   Barney, leave the girls alone!

see HERRING

IGNACE-HENRI-JEAN-THÉODORE FANTIN-LATOUR
1836 – 1904

Painter of still life and portraits; born Grenoble; worked in Paris and London; died in Buré.

1228   Roses

Red and pink roses in a vase on a table.

Canvas 16½ x 18¼ *ins.*, 42 x 47 *cms.*

Signed and dated, upper left: *Fantin 1881*

PROV.: Barbizon House, London, sold, 1930; Henry Van den Bergh, 1937, Mrs. S. Roskill.

LIT.: *Preview*, 105, 1974, pp. 939-43, illus. cover.

Presented by Mrs. Stephen Roskill through the National Art-Collections Fund from the collection of the late Henry Van den Bergh, 1973.   [*Plate 18*]

WILLIAM POWELL FRITH
1819 – 1909

Painter of narrative and historical genre; born at Aldfield near Ripon; worked in London, where he died.

337   Drovers in Glen Sligichan, Isle of Skye

see ANSDELL

Henry GARLAND
1834 – 1913

Genre and landscape painter; born in Hadlow, Kent; worked in Winchester and London.

251 Looking for the Mail Packet

An old gentleman, his wife and daughter on either side of him, stands on a hill scanning the horizon with a telescope.

Canvas 20½ x 18½ *ins., 52.1 x 46.9 cms.*

Signed and dated, lower left: *H. Garland 1861*

According to the artist's grand-son, H. J. Garland, the models for no.251 included the artist's mother, Elizabeth Garland, née Wilmot (1812-74), and his cousin, Mary Ann Garland (1845-1915), whom he married in 1877.

LIT.:   *York Catalogue*, 1907, no. 8; *Preview*, 76, 1966, illus. cover; C. Wood, *Dictionary of Victorian Painters*, 1971, illus. p. 273; H. J. Garland, letters in gallery files dated 24th May and 3rd June, 1974.

Burton Bequest, 1882.

Mark GERTLER
1891 – 1939

Figurative painter; born in London; worked in London, travelled in France and Spain; died in London.

439 The third Baron Derwent

Half-length seated figure looking left, holding a closed book on his knee, a book-case behind him.

Canvas 30 x 25 *ins., 76.2 x 63.5 cms.*

Signed, upper right: *Mark Gertler*

Painted at Hackness Hall, near Scarborough, in August 1933. According to Gertler's published letters written from Hackness Hall this portrait was nearly finished on 2nd August (to Koteliansky, 'I hope to finish the portrait tomorrow') and 24th August (to Balston, 'The portrait ought to be finished tomorrow'). Gertler was not happy with the commission; 'I really think I shall never again accept a commissioned portrait. It's a dreadful and degrading work' (to Balston, 31st August). He was happy, however, with Lord Derwent whom he found ' a genuine and a very decent young man, a great admirer of [D.H.] Lawrence' (to Koteliansky, 2nd August) and 'really nice —he is a genuine and simple person' (to Balston, 24th August).

George Harcourt Vanden-Bempde Johnstone, third Baron Derwent (1899-1949) of Hackness Hall was a considerable scholar, publishing books on Goya, 1930, and Rossini, 1934, as well as collections of his own poems, 1931 and 1945, and his reminiscences, *Return Ticket*, in 1940.

Gertler also made a pastel portrait of Lord Derwent, exhibited at the Leicester Galleries, October 1934, no. 106.

PROV.: The sitter.

LIT.: *Apollo*, October, 1934, p. 227, illus.; *Preview*, 11, 1950, p. 123, illus. cover; N. Carrington (ed.), *Gertler—Selected Letters*, 1965, pp. 236 (this letter, to Koteliansky, is dated 2nd August, 1932, but it must surely be 1933), 238; J. Woodeson, *Mark Gertler*, 1972, p. 386.

EXH.: London, Leicester Galleries, October, 1934 (99).

Presented by the sitter's cousins, Freda, Countess Listowel, and Lady Glynn, 1950.

SIR JOHN GILBERT
1817 – 1897

Narrative and history painter; born in Blackheath; worked in London.

351 Rembrandt's Studio

Interior of a large studio; Rembrandt stands painting at his easel, centre, looking at his model, left, an elderly lady (his mother?) in black who is attended by a maid (or Saskia); two gentlemen critics are seated behind the artist on the right.

Canvas 48 x 60 *ins.*, 121.9 x 152.5 *cms.*

Signed and dated, lower left: *John Gilbert 1869*

No.351 is a replica of the painting at the Towneley Hall Art Gallery, Burnley, which is signed and dated 1867 (exhibited R.A., 1867, no.564). Rembrandt's likeness seems founded on the etched 1639 *Self portrait* (Hind 168), and that of his mother apparently derives from his etching of 1631 (Hind 53).

PROV.: Joseph Craven sale, Christie's, 27th March, 1874 (178), bought Burton.

LIT.: *York Catalogue*, 1907, no. 20, illus. p. 17.

EXH.: York, 1879 (244).

Burton Bequest, 1882.

EDMUND GILL
1820 – 1894

Landscape painter; born in London; worked in Ludlow, Hereford and Birmingham; died in Hackbridge, Surrey.

293 Falls in the River Clyde, Corry Lynn, Scotland

A waterfall between rocks and trees.

Canvas 26 x 38 *ins.*, 66 x 96.5 *cms.*

Signed and dated, lower left: *E. Gill 1866*

PROV.: Joseph Craven sale, Christie's, 27th March, 1874 (154), bought Burton.

LIT.: *The Art Journal*, 1874, p. 43; *York Catalogue*, 1907, no. 54.

EXH.: R.A., 1866 (325); S.S., 1866-67 (243).

Burton Bequest, 1882.

Harold GILMAN
1876 – 1919

Painter of landscape and domestic genre; born at Rode, Somerset; worked in London, Gloucestershire and Kent; travelled to Odessa, America, Paris, Sweden and Norway; died in London.

209 The Artist's Daughters

Two small girls, one holding a doll, seated together in an armchair beside a window.

Canvas 24 x 18 *ins., 61 x 45.8 cms.*

Signed, lower right: *H. Gilman*

Painted c.1906-07. Previously called *The Twins,* this is a picture of Gilman's two daughters by his first marriage, Elizabeth and Hannah. They appear in several domestic scenes painted in Gilman's family home, Snargate Rectory, Kent (examples in Southampton Art Gallery and in the collection of Lord Walston), or in Sickert's house near Dieppe (Leeds Art Gallery), datable between 1906-07 and the winter of 1909-10 when Gilman's first wife, Grace, left for America with the two children.

PROV.: Mrs. Sylvia Gilman; Lefevre Gallery; Milner-White.

LIT:. *Preview,* 15, 1951, p. 178, illus.

EXH.: London, Lefevre Gallery, July, 1948 (11); Arts Council, *Gilman,* 1954-55 (12); Colchester, The Minories, *Gilman,* 1969 (6).

Presented by the Very Rev. E. Milner-White, 1950. [*Plate 34*]

725 Interior with Nude

A nude woman seated on a bed clasping one knee; a washing bowl in the left foreground and a chair and red curtain in the background.

Canvas 24 x 20 *ins., 61 x 50.8 cms.*

Signed, lower right: *H. Gilman*

Painted c.1914.

PROV.: Private collection; by 1953, Lefevre Gallery, 1955, bought Milner-White.

LIT.: J. Wood Palmer, *The Studio,* 149, June, 1955, p. 173, illus.; *Preview,* 31, 1955, p. 322, illus.

EXH.: London, Arts Council, *Camden Town Group,* 1953 (21), and *Gilman,* 1954-55 (26); Columbus, Ohio, *British Art 1890-1928,* 1971 (30).

Presented by the Very Rev. E. Milner-White, 1955. [*Plate 35*]

846 Beechwood, Gloucestershire

A beechwood in summer.

Canvas 24½ x 20 *ins., 61.6 x 50.8 cms.*

Signed, lower right: *H. Gilman*

Painted c.1917.

PROV.:   Mrs. Sylvia Gilman; 1948, Lefevre Gallery.
LIT.:   *Preview*, 31, 1955, p. 319, illus.
EXH.:   London, Lefevre Gallery, July, 1948 (29); Arts Council, *Camden Town Group,*
1953 (22)), and *Gilman*, 1954-55 (38), Dijon, 1957 (42).
Purchased, 1955.

CHARLES GINNER
1878 – 1952

Painter of still life and urban views; born in Cannes; worked in Paris and London, where he died.

855   Still life with flowers

Against a blue background stand pots of chrysanthemums and daffodils in a bowl.

Canvas 24 x 20 *ins.*, 61 x 50.8 *cms.*

Inscribed in pencil, verso: *No. 10 C. Ginner*

PROV.:   Yorkshire private collection; A. Coulter, York.
LIT.:   *Preview*, 105, 1974, p. 941, illus.
Purchased, 1955.

CHARLES GOGIN
1844 – 1931

History painter; born in London; worked in Paris and London; died in Reigate.

121   'And brief, good mother; for I am in haste'

From Shakespeare's *Richard III,* act IV, scene 4, line 162; Richard III on horseback with heralds and buglers, harangued by the old Duchess of York, left, and Elizabeth, Queen of Edward IV, who stands by her.

Millboard 14¾ x 12 *ins.*, 36.2 x 30.5 *cms.*

Painted in 1912.

PROV.:   Mrs. Gogin, the artist's widow.
EXH.:   London, Walker's Galleries, *Charles Gogin,* 1931 (17).
Presented by Mrs. Alma Gogin, 1935.

128   The Mother's Choice—the Scissors or the Sword

A scene from 6th-century Merovingian history; Clothilde (the widowed Queen of Clovis), seated centre, chooses between the scissors and the sword proferred by Clothar (one of her sons), foreground, as the instruments for

the fate of her three grandsons (orphaned by the death of their father Chlode-
mer), one of whom sits with a book on his knees on the left. The scissors
implied cutting the boys' hair, i.e. reducing them to plebeian rank; the sword
meant death, and was chosen by Clothilde.

Millboard 16 x 22½ *ins., 40.5 x 57.2 cms.*

Painted in 1883.

PROV.: Mrs. Gogin, the artist's widow.
EXH.: London, Walker's Galleries, *Charles Gogin,* 1931 (25).
Presented by Mrs. Alma Gogin, 1931.

215   Guy Fawkes

Guy Fawkes discovered in the vaults of the Houses of Parliament by the
Earl of Suffolk and a companion.

Card 6 x 11½ *ins., 15.2 x 28.6 cms.*

Painted in 1870.

PROV.: Mrs. Gogin, the artist's widow.
Presented by Mrs. Alma Gogin, 1936.

219   Red Rose

Head of a girl looking left, a red rose in her hair.

Millboard 14¾ x 14 *ins., 37.5 x 35.6 cms.*

Painted in 1898.

PROV.: Mrs. Gogin, the artist's widow.
EXH.: London, Walker's Galleries, *Charles Gogin,* 1931 (101).
Presented by Mrs. Alma Gogin, 1935.

SPENCER FREDERICK GORE
1878 – 1914

Painter of landscape and urban views; born in Epsom, Surrey; worked
in London, Somerset and Dorset; travelled in Spain; died in Richmond,
Surrey.

1035   From a canal bridge, Chalk Farm Road

A canal basin with barges in the foreground and a lock behind; factory
buildings and warehouses to the right.

Canvas 19 x 27 *ins., 43.3 x 68.6 cms.*

Stamped signature, lower left: *S. F. Gore*

A label verso, one of the series given by Gilman (q.v.) and the artist's
widow to the works by Gore in her possession at her husband's death, reads:
'Painted by S. F. Gore in 1913, from Canal Bridge in Chalk Farm Road.
Painted from drawings. 165a' [the 'a' crossed out]. A watercolour and a
squared-up drawing for the picture are in the possession of F. Gore.

PROV.: Bought from Mrs. Gore shortly after the artist's death by Milner-White; Ernest Gye, sold Sotheby's, 25th June, 1952 (125) as *The Regent Canal, Chalk Farm,* bought Leger; 1952, bought Milner-White.

LIT.: *Preview,* 67, 1964, p. 634, illus.

EXH.: London Group, March, 1914 (35), as *The Canal*; Colchester, The Minories, *Gore,* 1970 (57).

Presented by the Very Rev. E. Milner-White, 1963.   [*Plate 42*]

LAURA SYLVIA GOSSE
1881 – 1968

Painter of urban life; born in London, daughter of Sir Edmund Gosse; worked in London and Dieppe; died in London.

9 The Rural Postmen, Mantes-la-jolie

Three postmen walking across the town square with a tower of the Cathedral (?) behind them. Mantes-la-jolie is in the Ile-de-France.

Canvas 23 x 19 *ins.,* 58.5 x 48.3 *cms.*

Signed, lower left: *Gosse*

The title was given by the artist (letter in Gallery files dated 10th October, 1951); the picture had previously been called Dieppe. In a later letter (22nd February, 1965) Miss Gosse wrote that she 'thought it was painted towards the end of the thirties'.

PROV.: Kensington Art Gallery.

LIT.: *Preview,* 8, 1949, p. 88.

EXH.: London, Kensington Art Gallery, 1948; Dijon, 1957 (41).

Purchased, 1949.

SIR FRANCIS GRANT
1803 – 1878

Portrait painter; born in Kilgraston, Perthshire; worked in London; died in Melton Mowbray.

1221 The second Earl de Grey

Whole-length figure in full regimentals as Colonel of the Yorkshire Yeomanry; he carries his hat under his right arm and holds his sword hilt with his left hand; a landscape view in the right background.

Canvas 96 x 60 *ins.,* 244 x 152.4 *cms.*

The sitter appears in Grant's *Sitter Book* (MS. in National Portrait Gallery archive) in September 1848; 'The Earl de Grey, Painted for the Yorkshire Yeomanry, Full length, in regimentals, £315'. The portrait was commissioned by the officers of the regiment for their newly-completed mess in the De Grey

Rooms, York, where it was first hung on 4th December, 1849, as a 'mark of affection and regard' (from the original plaque attached to the frame). A mezzotint of no.1221 by S. W. Reynolds was published by Colnaghi on 1st October, 1850.

Thomas Philip, second Earl de Grey (1781-1859), soldier, statesman and antiquary, was the eldest son of Thomas Robinson, second Baron Grantham. He succeeded in 1786, and in 1792 he also became the sixth Baronet Robinson. In 1803 he assumed the surname of Weddell; in 1833 he became the third Baron Lucas and succeeded his maternal aunt, the Countess de Grey, as the second Earl de Grey, altering his surname again to de Grey. He married in 1805 Henrietta Cole and was survived by two daughters. He was the first President of the R.I.B.A. 1834, Lord Lieutenant of Ireland 1841-44, and was created K.G. in 1844. His Yorkshire residences were Newby Hall and Newby Park (alias Baldersby), both confusingly called Newby in his time.

Other portraits of Earl de Grey were drawn by Ingres in 1816 (Newby Hall), and painted by Lawrence before 1806 (Woodyates Manor), J. Wood before 1837 (R.I.B.A.), and J. Lucas in 1832 and F. R. Say in 1839 (respectively Christie's, 16th November, 1917, lots 88 and 111).

PROV.: The Yorkshire Yeomanry, York (De Grey Rooms, 1848-1905, Yorkshire Club, 1905-72).

LIT.: *Preview*, 101, 1973, pp. 907-10, illus.

Purchased, 1972. [*Plate 1*]

WALTER GREAVES
1846 – 1930

Painter of London life; born in Chelsea; worked in London; died in a Chelsea alms house.

10 Japanese figures on Chelsea Embankment

Three ladies in the foreground playing ball on the railed embankment by the Thames.

Canvas 15 x 12 *ins.*, 38.1 x 30.5 *cms.*

The smooth, thinly painted technique of no.10 suggests a date in the 1870s; Whistler's *Variations in Violet and Green* of 1871 (private collection, U.S.A.) shows a more sophisticated use of the same motifs.

PROV.: MacDonald; Roland, Browse and Delbanco, 1948, bought Milner-White.

LIT.: *Preview*, 2, 1948, illus. cover.

EXH.: Dijon, 1957 (33).

Presented by the Very Rev. E. Milner-White, 1948. [*Plate 20*]

1028 Nocturne in blue and gold

The Thames at dusk, looking up Battersea Reach from Chelsea; two barges, right, and two figures in the right foreground.

Canvas 12 x 18 *ins.,* 30.5 x 45.7 *cms.*

Until now attributed to Whistler, but the slightly coarse brushwork and the hard quality of no.1028 suggest that it is either by Greaves at his most Whistlerian in the 1870s, or that it is one of those Whistler canvases taken at the time of his bankruptcy in 1879 which reappeared at Dowdeswells in 1910, some sadly restored, others re-worked by Greaves (see E. J. and J. Pennell, *The Whistler Journal,* Philadelphia, 1921, pp. 125-44).

Closely comparable compositions by Whistler are the *Nocturne in blue and silver no. 1* (illus. Pennell, f.p. 120) and the *Nocturne in blue and silver: Cremorne Lights* (Tate Gallery 3420), dated 1872. A close imitation by Greaves of the former painting is now in the collection of T. Pocock (illus., Pennell, f.p. 120).

PROV.: Dix, bought Roland, Browse and Delbanco; 1950, bought Milner-White.

LIT.: *Preview,* 63, 1963, p. 596, illus., as Whistler.

EXH.: London, Roland, Browse and Delbanco, *English and French Painting,* 1950 (30), lent Milner-White; Arts Council, *The Thames in Art,* 1967 (34); Guildhall Gallery, *London and the Greater Painters,* 1971 (29).

Presented by the Very Rev. E. Milner-White, 1963.

WEEDON GROSSMITH
1854 – 1919

Genre painter; born in London; worked in London; travelled in England as an actor; died in London.

690 Girl with a kettle

A young girl, half-length facing spectator, with a bonnet and shawl, holding a kettle, umbrella and a bundle of clothes.

Canvas 27 x 20 *ins.,* 68.6 x 50.8 *cms.*

Signed and dated, lower left: *Weedon Grossmith/1888*

After studying as a painter at the R.A. schools and the Slade, Grossmith started his theatrical career in 1885. In his autobiography *From Studio to Stage,* 1913, he records that he returned to painting again in 1887-88 and 'painted two or three pot-boilers and luckily sold them' (p. 169). Though the subject of this picture appears specifically theatrical (a premature Eliza Doolittle) a literary source has not been discovered.

PROV:. A. Coulter, York.

LIT.: *Preview,* 25, 1954, p. 264, illus. cover.

EXH.: Dijon, 1957 (34).

Purchased, 1953.

[Plate 30]

Alvaro GUEVARA
1894 – 1951

Painter of still life and genre; born in Valparaiso, Chile; worked in Bradford, London, Chile and France; died in Aix-en-Provence.

1036 Still Life

A dish of oysters, a shallow bowl with an onion and an overturned tankard on a table.

Millboard 19½ x 19½ *ins.*, 49.6 x 49.6 *cms.*

PROV.: The artist's widow; Mayor Gallery, 1952, bought Milner-White.
EXH.: London, Mayor Gallery, *Guevara*, 1952 (25).
Presented by the Very Rev. E. Milner-White, 1963.

Jean-Baptiste-Antoine GUILLEMET
1843 – 1918

Landscape painter; born in Chantilly; worked in Paris and on the Normandy coast; died at Dordogne.

971 Artist in a landscape

A windy day on a rough heath with a painter seated at his easel, right.

Canvas 15 x 21½ *ins.*, 38.1 x 54.6 *cms.*

Signed, lower right: *A. Guillemet*

PROV.: Galerie des Beaux-Arts, Paris; Roland, Browse and Delbanco.
EXH.: London, Roland, Browse and Delbanco, May-June, 1960 (40).
Purchased, 1961.

Johannes Hubertus Leonardus de HAAS
1832 – 1908

Born in Hedel, near 's Hertogenbosch, Holland; worked in Amsterdam, Haarlem, Oostebeek and Brussels; died in Königswinter, Germany.

356 Pasturage in Holland

A group of three cows and a bull beside a stream in a meadow with pollarded willows.

Canvas 31¾ x 59½ *ins.*, 80.6 x 151.1 *cms.*

Signed, lower right: *J H/de Haas,* and dated 1868 on warranty label, verso, which is inscribed *Bruxelles.*

LIT.: *York Catalogue*, 1907, no. 36, illus. p. 25.
Burton Bequest, 1882.

Frederick Daniel HARDY
1826 – 1911

Genre and narrative painter; born at Windsor; worked at Cranbrook and in London.

246 The Three Orphans

Cottage interior with a woman seated sewing at a table, watching two children, left, near a hearth; the boy kneeling feeds a fledgling with a spoon, the little girl seated on stool holds a bowl.

Panel 10½ x 14 ins., 26.7 x 35.6 cms.

Signed and dated, lower right: *F. D. Hardy. 1860.*

Lit.: *York Catalogue*, 1907, no. 108.

Exh.: York, 1866 (204), lent Burton, and 1879 (280), lent Mrs, Burton.

Burton Bequest, 1882.

271 The Volunteers

Cottage interior with group of children playing; one beating a drum, the others watching a boy wearing a busby; a soldier sits in the background with a child who plays with a medal on his uniform; beside him a man stands holding a pipe and a woman sits by the fire.

Panel 25 x 44½ ins., 63.5 x 113.5 cms.

Signed and dated, upper left: *F. D. Hardy. 1860.*

Lit.: *York Catalogue*, 1907, no. 112; C. Wood, *Dictionary of Victorian Painters*, 1971, p. 282, illus.

Exh.: R.A., 1860 (119); York, 1879 (183), lent Burton.

Burton Bequest, 1882.

Henri HAYDEN
1883 – 1970

Painter of landscape and still life; born in Warsaw; worked in Warsaw, Paris and the south of France; died in France.

965 St-Lunaire

An angular composition of a hilly seaside town with a church; a stone bridge in the foreground.

Canvas 35½ x 28½ ins., 90.2 x 72.4 cms.

Signed and dated, lower right: *Hayden 1914*

According to the artist (letter to Leslie Waddington, April 1961) this picture 'was painted in 1914 just before the declaration of war at St. Lunaire near Dinard, a little beach on the Atlantic'.

Prov.: Roland, Browse and Delbanco.

Lit.: *Preview,* 52, 1960, pp. 499-503, illus.; J. Selz, *Hayden,* Geneva, 1962, pl. 12.

Exh.: London, Roland, Browse and Delbanco, October-November, 1955 (22), as *Brittany village with church and bridge,* and June-July, 1957 (27); Waddington Galleries, *Hayden,* 1962 (8).

Purchased with the aid of a grant from the Calouste Gulbenkian Foundation, 1960.

[*Plate 36*]

John William HAYNES
active 1852 – 1882

Painter of domestic genre; worked in London.

170 The First, the Only One

Cottage interior with a woman seated, left, by a baby in a cradle; a bird cage hangs from a rafter.

Canvas 16 x 16 *ins.,* 40.7 x 40.7 *cms.* (circular)

Signed and dated, lower right: *J. W. Haynes 59*

Prov.: Anon. sale, Christie's, 17th April, 1866 (128), as *An Interior,* bought Burton.

Lit.: *The Art Journal,* 1860, p. 170; *York Catalogue,* 1907, no. 9; C. Wood, *Dictionary of Victorian Painters,* 1971, illus. p. 284.

Exh.: R. A. 1860 (391), as *The Mother.*

Burton Bequest, 1882.

Isaac HENZELL
active 1854 – 1875

Genre painter; worked in London.

350 The Young Fisherman

A seated woman knitting on the sea-shore with two children beside her, one with a fisherman's basket on his back; hills to the right and a man and woman gathering shellfish, left.

Canvas 44 x 34 *ins.,* 111.8 x 86.4 *cms.*

Signed and dated, lower right: *I Henzell/1862*

Lit.: *York Catalogue,* 1907, no. 55.

Burton Bequest, 1882.

340 Feeding the Pets
see BRIGHT

Auguste HERBIN
1882 – 1960

Cubist and abstract painter; born at Quiévy near Cambrai; worked and died in Paris.

1020 Arum Lilies

On a green table, a brown two-handled pitcher, left, and yellow arum lilies in a red vase, right.

Canvas 28½ x 23 *ins.,* 72.4 x 58.5 *cms.*

Signed, lower right: *Herbin*

Probably painted c.1911.

PROV.:   A German private collection; Roland, Browse and Delbanco.

LIT.:   *Preview,* 61, 1963, pp. 581-83, illus.

EXH.:   Hanover, Kestner Gesellschaft, 1919; London, Roland, Browse and Delbanco, April-May, 1961 (31).

Purchased with the aid of a grant from the Victoria and Albert Museum, 1962.

Josef HERMAN
1911 –

Painter of industrial and urban life; born in Warsaw; has worked in Warsaw, Brussels, Glasgow, South Wales, London and Suffolk.

978 Digging for roots

Dark heavy figures bending down picking roots in a ploughed field.

Canvas 25 x 30 *ins.,* 63.5 x 76.2 *cms.*

Painted in 1949 when the artist was living in Ystradgynlais in South Wales.

PROV.:   The artist, September, 1950, bought R. D. S. May; 1953, Gimpel Fils; Dr. Ettlinger (later Mrs. Josef Herman); Roland, Browse and Delbanco.

EXH.:   London, Gimpel Fils, November, 1953 (13), as *Peasants picking roots*; Whitechapel Art Gallery, *Herman,* 1956 (20), lent Dr. Ettlinger.

Purchased with the aid of a grant from the Calouste Gulbenkian Foundation, 1961.

John Frederick HERRING
1795 – 1865

Animal painter; born in Blackfriars; worked in Doncaster and the midlands; died in Tunbridge.

147 Barney, leave the girls alone!

In a rolling landscape, a young man blows pipe smoke into a girl's face but is restrained by a second girl; two harnessed carthorses stand to the right.

Canvas 34 x 44 *ins.,* 86.4 x 111.8 *cms.*

Signed and dated, lower right: *J. F. Herring Senr. 1850*

Relined, 1973.

In 1883 the picture was exhibited in York as *Paddy, leave the girls alone!*
The figures have traditionally been attributed to Thomas Faed (q.v.),
and a note exists in Faed's record book (MS. in National Gallery of Scotland
archive) to the effect that he painted in the figures on Herring's 'picture for
Mr. Lloyd' in 1852; he possibly mistook the date, since the record book was
compiled at the end of his life.

PROV.: Lloyd (?).

LIT.: *York Catalogue*, 1907, no. 111, as Herring; *Preview*, 76, 1966, p. 707, illus.;
C. Wood, *Dictionary of Victorian Painters,* 1971, p. 65.

EXH.: S.S., 1851 (431), as Herring.

Burton Bequest, 1882. [*Plate 6*]

JAMES JOHN HILL
1811 – 1882

Genre painter; born in Birmingham; worked in Birmingham and London;
travelled in Ireland.

1010 Boy and dog reposing

A barefoot boy in ragged trousers and a red waistcoat seated on a bank
with a collie dog beside him; landscape background right.

Panel 14 x 11¾ ins., 35.6 x 29.8 cms.

PROV.: H. J. Ware, by descent.

EXH.: York, 1866 (311), lent H. J. Ware.

Presented by Col. N. Innes Ware, 1962.

267 The Cottage Door

see BRIGHT

TRISTRAM HILLIER
1905 –

Landscape painter; born in Peking; has worked in Cambridge, London,
Paris, the south of France and Somerset.

208 Haymaking

Haycarts and agricultural implements, foreground; a church and trees,
far distance; birds flying overhead.

Canvas 23½ x 31½ ins., 59.7 x 80.1 cms.

Signed, lower right: *Hillier,* inscribed verso: *Aug' 43*

PROV.: The artist; C.A.S.

EXH.: London, Tate Gallery, C.A.S., *Contemporary Paintings III*, 1945 (16).

Presented by the Contemporary Art Society, 1946.

THOMAS CHRISTOPHER HOFLAND
1777 – 1843

Landscape painter; born at Worksop; worked in London, travelled in England and Italy; died in Florence.

1011   Moonlit landscape

A castle, left, with a bridge, river and boats, centre, under a moonlit sky.

Board 11¾ x 18 *ins.,* 29.8 x 45.7 *cms.*

PROV.: H. J. Ware, by descent.

Presented by Col. N. Innes Ware, 1962.

EDWARD HENRY HOLDER
active 1864 – 1917

Landscape painter; born at Scarborough; worked in London, Reigate and in South Africa.

200   On the road to Llyn Elsi, Bettws-y-Coed, North Wales

Landscape with rocks and trees; on the right, two figures seated between trees.

Card 13½ x 18¼ *ins.,* 34.3 x 46.4 *cms.*

Signed, bottom right: *E. H. Holder '85,* inscribed with title, verso.

Bequeathed by Major R. W. Richardson, 1916.

202   Rievaulx Abbey, near Helmsley, Yorkshire, from the south

Figures on a foreground grassy slope; a view through trees of the Abbey.

Canvas 30 x 20 *ins.,* 76.2 x 50.8 *cms.*

Signed and dated, lower right: *E. H. Holder. 1880*

LIT.: *York Catalogue,* 1907, no. 51.

Burton Bequest, 1882.

243   Cornelian Bay, Scarborough

Cliffs, left, and boulders, foreground, with figures collecting driftwood on the rocky beach beyond.

Canvas 14 x 24 *ins.,* 35.6 x 60.9 *cms.*

Signed and dated, lower left: *E. H. Holder. 1878*

LIT.: *York Catalogue,* 1907, no. 68.

Burton Bequest, 1882.

264 Landscape

A broad stream, foreground, with figures on bank to the left; a wooden bridge centre; trees and farm in the right middleground; village and hills in the background.

Canvas 20 x 30 *ins., 50.8 x 76.2 cms.*

Signed and dated, lower left: *E. H. Holder. 1880*

LIT.: *York Catalogue,* 1907, no. 105.

Burton Bequest, 1882.

279 View on the River Derwent at Fisherman's Bridge, Forge Valley, near Scarborough

A woman seated reading and a boy with a bunch of flowers by an old tree, foreground; beyond, a stream with a weir; a wooded meadow with sheep in the background.

Canvas 20 x 30 *ins., 50.8 x 76.2 cms.*

Signed and dated, lower right: *E. H. Holder. 1880*

LIT.: *York Catalogue,* 1907, no. 82.

Burton Bequest, 1882.

281 Scene on the River Conway, Bettws-y-Coed, North Wales

Broad shallow river with three cows in the foreground; a sunlit meadow and wooded hills beyond; sunset sky.

Canvas 18 x 32 *ins., 45.7 x 81.3 cms.*

Signed and dated, lower right: *E. H. Holder. 1880*

LIT.: *York Catalogue,* 1907, no. 12.

Burton Bequest, 1882.

298 Hackness Wood, near Scarborough

A stream in the foreground, right; a meadow with cattle and sheep, left, and wooded slopes beyond.

Canvas 18 x 32 *ins., 45.7 x 81.3 cms.*

Signed, dated and inscribed, lower left: *E. H. Holder. 1880 Scarboro'*

LIT.: *York Catalogue,* 1907, no. 104.

Burton Bequest, 1882.

299 On the Yorkshire Coast

Rocky shore with waves breaking in the foreground; sunlit cliffs beyond.

Canvas 20 x 30 *ins., 50.8 x 76.2 cms.*

Signed and dated, lower left: *E. H. Holder. 1873*

LIT.: *York Catalogue,* 1907, no. 53.

Burton Bequest, 1882.   [*Plate 12*]

456 The Yorkshire Coast

Evening landscape with sloping cliffs, right and centre, with figures; sea with sailing boats, left.

Canvas 18 x 32 *ins., 45.7 x 81.3 cms.*

Signed and dated, lower left: *E. H. Holder 1880*

LIT.:   *York Catalogue,* 1907, no. 58.
Burton Bequest, 1882.

DUDLEY HOLLAND
1915 – 1956

Figurative painter; worked in London, York 1949-51, and Guildford; died near Guildford.

578 Art Gallery: Transition

Interior of York Art Gallery; a view from the first floor landing, down the staircase, with scaffolding, steps and a broom; the stair-well was being re-painted in mid 1949 while the first floor gallery was being refurbished.

Canvas 24 x 30 *ins., 61 x 76.2 cms.*

Signed and dated, lower left: *D Holland '50*

EXH.:   York, *Holland and Wright,* 1950 (7); Cambridge, Arts Council, 1950 (4).
Presented by friends of the artist, 1951.

JOHN HOLLAND
active 1830 – 1886

Genre and narrative painter; born and worked in Nottingham.

127 The Fight for the Platform

The Great Market Place at Nottingham, with figures tearing up cobble stones in the foreground and broken chairs and placards strewn on the ground; two factions fight around a raised platform, left and centre, with groups of fleeing figures, right; a crowd armed with staves in the background.

Canvas 12 x 18 *ins., 30.5 x 45.8 cms.*

Signed, lower right: *J Holland*

Also known as *Nottingham Lambs,* no.127 was painted in 1865, depicting a riot which took place at Nottingham on 26th June, 1865, during the elections, of which the following description appeared in the *Illustrated London News,* 8th July, 1865: 'An open air meeting of the electors and non-electors had assembled in the Great Market to hear addresses from Messrs. Morley and Paget. The operative framework knitters of Sutton-in-Ashfield, Kirkby and other villages were to come by special train to take part in the proceedings. When the train arrived, the operatives were set upon by a violent rabble and driven back into the station. Numbers of roughs waited in various avenues in the town for Messrs. Paget and Morley, but they did not make their appearance. Ultimately the hustings were got possession of, the flags were torn down, the scaffolding set fire to and totally consumed, the rabble pelted the friends of Mr. Morley with stones and several persons were seriously injured'. The result of the election, held on 14th July, 1865, was: Samuel Morley (Lib.) and Sir Robert Suckles Clifton (Lib.-Con.) elected; Charles Paget (Lib.) and A. G. Marten (Con.) defeated.

A related engraving which appeared in the *Illustrated London News*, 8th July, 1865, shows more of the north side of the Great Market Place.

LIT.:   *York Catalogue*, 1907, no. 81.

EXH.:   B.I., 1866 (481); York, 1880 (134), lent Burton; Nottingham Castle, Festival Exhibition, 1971.

Burton Bequest, 1882.

JOHN CALLCOTT HORSLEY
1817 – 1903

Genre and history painter; born in London; worked in London and Cranbrook, Kent.

494 The Interior of the Great Hall, Haddon: Rent Day

Interior of a medieval timbered hall; a 16th-century scene, with a clerk seated at a table, left, taking rent payments from the tenants who come through a door on the right.

Canvas 14 x 14 ins., 35.6 x 35.6 cms.

Signed and dated, lower right: *J. C. Horsley/RA/1866*

Presumably a sketch for the larger picture of the same subject (51 x 51 ins.) dated 1868, exhibited at the R.A. in 1904, (and presumably also the picture exhibited by Horsley at the R.A. in 1868, no. 302). He had previously treated this subject in a picture exhibited at the B.I. in 1837, no.182, when he was only twenty. Haddon Hall in Derbyshire, formerly the home of the Vernon and Manners families, was the original of Martindale Hall in Walter Scott's *Peveril of the Peak*, 1822; (see also D. Pasmore, no.269).

PROV.:   Joseph Craven sale, Christie's, 27th March, 1874 (153), bought Burton.

LIT.:   *York Catalogue*, 1907, no. 13.

EXH.:   London, Whitechapel Art Gallery, *Pageant Exhibition*, 1909 (15).

Burton Bequest, 1882.

Eugène-Gabriel ISABEY
1803 – 1886

Marine and genre painter; born in Paris; worked in Paris and Normandy; travelled in Algeria; died at Laguy near Paris.

1117   Boat in a Storm

Sailing boat in heavy, stormy, seas trailing a smaller dinghy with two men; a heavy sky beyond.

Canvas 48 x 37 *ins.,* 122 x 94 *cms.*

Signed, lower left: *EI*

Painted c.1850-55.

Prov.:   Roland, Browse and Delbanco.

Lit.:   *Apollo,* June, 1965, pp. 445-46, illus.; *Preview,* 71, 1965, pp. 666-68, illus.

Exh.:   London, Roland, Browse and Delbanco, *From Géricault to Courbet,* 1965 (34).

Purchased with the aid of a grant from the Victoria and Albert Museum, 1965.

[Plate 5 and cover]

Richard JACK
1866 – 1952

Portrait and landscape painter; born in Sunderland; worked in York 1882-86, London and Paris; emigrated to Canada c.1930; died in Montreal.

182   Landscape

Field with a haystack, right; a wood in the middle distance; cloudy sky.

Canvas 20 x 24 *ins.,* 50.8 x 61 *cms.*

Signed, lower left: *R. Jack*

Presented by Lady Atcherley, 1938.

192   Boats on the river at Acaster Malbis, York

River scene with jetty, figures and boats; trees and houses in the background right: Acaster Malbis is a small village on the river Ouse, south-east of York.

Millboard 14½ x 21¼ *ins.,* 36.8 x 54 *cms.*

Signed and dated, lower left: *R. Jack./'84*

Prov.:   Headley, York.

Purchased, 1939.

317 The Burial of Siegfried

Six warriors with spears bearing the body, centre, preceded by another carrying a spear, right, and followed by two helmeted warriors bearing a sword and a helmet, left; twilight sky beyond; the subject is adapted from Wagner's *Ring*, 'The Twilight of the Gods', act III.

Canvas 51 x 72 *ins.*, 130 x 183 *cms.*

Signed and dated, lower right: *R. Jack. 1920*

EXH.: R.A., 1920 (599), as *The Passing of the Chieftain.*

Presented by the artist, 1928.

395 The Return to the Front: Victoria Railway Station

Victoria Station, London; a crowded platform scene with soldiers and their relatives; girl with a tray of magazines, centre.

Canvas 80 x 125½ *ins.*, 203.3 x 319 *cms.*

Signed and dated, lower left: *R. Jack 1916*

EXH.: R.A., 1916 (579); Clapham, British Rail Board, July, 1965 onwards.

Presented by the artist, 1928.

495 Moulin de Coty, Cahors

A stream with a fisherman, left foreground; mill and buildings background; Cahors is on the river Lot near Villefranche in the Guyen.

Canvas 19 x 24½ *ins.*, 48.3 x 62.2 *cms.*

Signed, lower right: *R. Jack*

Painted c.1924.

PROV.: The artist.

EXH.: London, Fine Art Society, *Jack*, 1925 (41); York, March-April, 1925.

Purchased, 1925.

1015 Henry John Ware

Half-length, full-face, of a white-haired elderly man wearing a black bow, high wing collar and a black jacket.

Canvas 30 x 25 *ins.*, 76.2 x 63.5 *cms.*

Signed and dated, lower right: *R. Jack. 1890*

H. J. Ware (1824-1902) was a York solicitor, the godson of John Brooke the distinguished solicitor whose portrait by William Etty is also in the gallery (no.982). Ware joined Brooke's firm c.1844, later became his partner and after his death succeeded as head of the firm. In 1882 he was one of John Burton's three executors.

PROV.: H. J. Ware, by descent.

Presented by Col. N. Innes Ware, 1962.

FREDERICK WILLIAM JACKSON
1859 – 1918

Landscape painter; born at Middleton Junction, Oldham; worked in Oldham, Manchester, Paris and in Hinderwell, Yorkshire; travelled in Morocco and Italy.

1168 Ships in Venice

Moored sailing ships with figures in a dinghy alongside; the Church of S. Giorgio Maggiore in the background, right.

Millboard 8⅝ x 10⅜ *ins., 22 x 26.5 cms.*

Signed, lower left: *F W J*

Jackson exhibited *At Venice* at the R.A. in 1893, which might indicate a date for no.1168.

PROV.: Walter Butterworth, by descent.

Presented by L. M. Angus-Butterworth in memory of his father Walter Butterworth, J.P., a patron of the arts, 1969.

GWEN JOHN
1876 – 1939

Painter of portraits and domestic genre; born in Haverfordwest, Pembrokeshire, sister of Augustus John; worked in London and Paris; died at Dieppe.

867 Young woman in a red shawl

Three-quarter length seated young woman in a red shawl facing left, her hands clasped in her lap.

Canvas 17¾ x 13¾ *ins., 45.1 x 34.9 cms.*

Signed, lower right: *G. John*

Probably painted c.1912 when Gwen John is known to have been working on a painting of a woman in a red shawl. Several versions of the picture exist; a smaller one (canvas 9⅞ x 7⅞ ins.) is in the collection of the Duke of Devonshire, and another slightly less finished version (canvas 17½ x 13½ ins.), formerly in the collection of Lady Adeane, was sold at Christie's, 29th October, 1971, lot 154. The model was one of the artist's regular sitters and appears in almost identical positions in a number of other pictures.

PROV.: Matthiesen Gallery, 1946; 1952, bought Milner-White.

LIT.: *Preview,* 34, 1956, p. 341, illus. cover.

EXH.: London, Matthiesen Gallery, *Gwen John,* 1946 (37); Arts Council, *British Painting 1925-50,* 1951 (64); Dijon, 1957 (38); R.A., 1962 (269).

Presented by the Very Rev. E. Milner-White, 1956.   *[Plate 38]*

Alexander JOHNSTON
1815 – 1891

Genre and narrative painter; born in Edinburgh; worked in Edinburgh and London.

160 On the Balcony

A woman in a plaid standing on a terrace with a stone balustrade; trees and a castle beyond.

Canvas 13 x 10 *ins.,* 33 x 25.4 *cms.*

Signed, lower left: *A S* and (partly painted out) *A J* (?)

Early York exhibition catalogues give the title as *Tartana*. Originally attributed to Alexander Johnston, the attribution was later changed (through a misreading of the initial J as 'S'), improbably, to Abraham Solomon. Probably identical with the painting *Tartana* exhibited by Johnston in 1863 (see below) with verses from Allan Ramsay: 'Her plaid round her modest face, saves blushes with the gayest grace'.

LIT.: *York Catalogue,* 1907, no. 63, as Solomon.
EXH.: (possibly) B.I., 1863 (101), as *Tartana* by Johnston.
Burton Bequest, 1882.

Thomas Musgrove JOY
1812 – 1866

Painter of domestic genre; born at Boughton Monchelsea, Kent; worked in London.

169 The Mother

A richly furnished interior with a young woman seated by an open window showing a locket to a baby on her knee.

Canvas 24 x 20 *ins.,* 61 x 50.8 *cms.*

Signed and dated, lower right: *T M Joy/1847*

LIT.: *York Catalogue,* 1907, no. 31; C. Wood, *Dictionary of Victorian Painters,* 1971, p. 78.
EXH.: B.I., 1848 (159), with quotation: 'And joyful in a mother's gentlest cares,/ Blest cares all other feeling far above/Herself more sweetly rears the babe she bears'/ . . .
Burton Bequest, 1882.

Stanislawa de KARLOWSKA
1876 – 1952

Painter of landscape and still life; born at Czeliewy, Poland; worked in Warsaw, Cracow, Paris and London; married the English painter Robert Bevan; died in London.

1141   Green Apples

Green apples and beans on a checked table-cloth with a basket of apples behind.

Canvas 13¼ x 15¼ *ins., 33.7 x 38.7 cms.*

Signed, lower right: *S. de Karlowska*

Painted c.1921.

PROV.: Mrs. E. H. Baty, the artist's daughter.

LIT.: *Preview,* 83, 1968, p. 762.

EXH.: London, Goupil Gallery, November-December, 1921 (205), as *Apples;* Anglo-Polish Society, *Robert Bevan and Stanislawa de Karlowska,* 1968 (39).

Presented by Mrs. E. H. Baty, on behalf of the artist's family, 1968.

BRYAN KNEALE
1930 –

Figurative and abstract artist; born in Douglas, Isle of Man; has worked in Douglas, London and in Italy.

960   Sir Herbert Read

Half-length figure to left, wearing a bow tie.

Canvas 40 x 29½ *ins., 101.6 x 75 cms.*

Signed and dated, upper right: *Bryan Kneale 58*

Sir Herbert Read (1893-1968), the noted poet, philosopher and aesthetician, was born and died at Kirbymoorside, York. He was the first President of the Friends of York Art Gallery.

PROV.: Redfern Gallery.

EXH.: Douglas, Manx Museum, *Kneale,* 1963 (5).

Presented by the Friends of York Art Gallery, 1960.

WILLIAM ADOLPHUS KNELL
c.1805 – 1875

Marine painter; worked and died in London; travelled in northern Europe.

119   Fishing boats off the French coast beating to windward

A stormy sea with a rowing boat, centre, a jetty, with figures, left; a sailing boat, right, and a steamer in the background.

Canvas 10 x 20 *ins., 25.4 x 50.8 cms.*

LIT.: *York Catalogue,* 1907, no. 14; C. Wood, *Dictionary of Victorian Painters,* 1971, p. 80.

EXH.: (possibly) R.A., 1827 (485), as *French Boats off Boulogne coast.*

Burton Bequest, 1882.

383 Entering Portsmouth Harbour

A man-of-war entering a harbour beyond; a boat with women and sailors in the foreground with other shipping in the middle distance; evening sky.

Canvas 30 x 50 *ins., 76.2 x 127 cms.*

Signed, lower right: *W. A. Knell*

A label, verso, gives the title as *Looking into Portsmouth Harbour—two 90 gun ships entering.* On the label Knell also styles himself 'Marine Painter to Her Majesty', which might suggest a date post 1857 when he painted *The Landing of the Prince Regent at Dover* for Queen Victoria.

Bequeathed by Mrs. Hannah Deighton, 1913. [*Plate 15*]

John Prescott KNIGHT
1803 – 1881

Portrait and history painter; born in Stafford; worked and died in London.

656 Christ appearing to Mary Magdalene

Before the empty cavernous tomb, right, Mary Magdalene, centre, kneels before the risen Christ who stands in the left. The scene illustrates John XX, verses 16-17, which are inscribed, verso.

Panel 27¾ x 35¾ *ins., 70.5 x 90.8 cms.*

Painted c.1840. Probably inspired by William Etty's *Christ appearing to Mary Magdalene after the Resurrection* (Tate Gallery 362) which was commissioned by John Turrill to be engraved as an illustration for *The Sacred Annual for 1834* (see D. Farr, *Etty,* 1958, pl. 54b).

PROV.: J. P. Knight sale, Christie's, 2nd July, 1881 (76), bought Mendoza; Appleby's.

LIT.: *Preview,* 22, 1953, p. 238, as Etty, and 28, 1954, p. 291, illus., as Knight; D. Farr, *William Etty,* 1958, pp. 69-70, pl. 54a; H. Dyson, *The Works of J. P. Knight,* Stafford Historical and Civic Society, 1971, no. 78.

EXH.: R.A., 1841 (270); B.I., 1842 (241); Stafford Art Gallery, *Knight,* October-November, 1963 (8).

Purchased, 1952.

George LANCE
1802 – 1864

Painter of still life; born at Little Easton, Essex; worked in Liverpool and London; died in Birkenhead.

241 Still life with dead game

A dead mallard duck on a wooden ledge, with onions, a large green jar and a basket draped with a white cloth on which lie a sprig of holly and a bunch of purple grapes.

Canvas 17½ x 14 *ins.*, 44.5 x 35.6 *cms.*

Signed and dated, lower left: *G Lance 1843*

LIT.: *York Catalogue*, 1907, no. 67.

EXH.: (possibly) B.I., 1844 (17).

Burton Bequest, 1882. [*Plate 2*]

EDWARD LE BAS
1904 – 1966

Painter of urban life; born in London; worked in London, Majorca and France.

14 Fish Market, Dieppe

A fish stall behind which stand two women, centre, and a man, right; an old woman looks at the fish and a child stands in the foreground right.

Millboard 19 x 23½ *ins.*, 48.3 x 59.7 *cms.*

Signed, lower right: *E le Bas*

Painted in 1948; a study for a large painting, *The Fish Market, Dieppe* exhibited at the R.A. in 1949 and now in the Art Gallery of New South Wales.

PROV.: The artist; Leicester Galleries.

LIT.: *Preview*, 4, 1948, illus. cover.

EXH.: Peterlee, Arts Council, *British Painters of Today*, 1955 (16).

Purchased from the G. J. Wolstenholme Bequest, 1948.

FRANÇOIS-LOUIS LENFANT (or LANFANT) called LENFANT DE METZ
1814 – 1892

Painter of domestic genre; born at Bierck, near Metz; worked in Paris and Le Havre where he died.

164 The Picture Book

An interior with two children, in tunics and gaiters, seated on a chair draped with a rug looking at a sketchbook.

Canvas 24 x 19½ *ins.*, 61 x 49.5 *cms.*

Signed, lower right: *Lanfant de Metz*

PROV.: George Taylor sale, Christie's, 14th May, 1860 (206).

LIT.: *York Catalogue*, 1907, no. 97.

Burton Bequest, 1882.

Robert C. LESLIE
active 1843 – 1887

Marine painter; eldest son of C. R. Leslie; worked in London and South-ampton.

1042 A Squall, Southampton Water

A choppy sea with three fishing boats; a town with a church spire in the background.

Canvas 33 x 60 *ins.,* 74 x 152.4 *cms.*

Signed, lower right; *Robᵗ· Leslie.,* and inscribed, verso: *Squall. Southampton Water 1885.* and with artist's address: *6, Moira Place, Southampton.*

Exh.: R.A., 1885 (755).

Presented by the Very Rev. E. Milner-White, 1963.

John LINNELL
1792 – 1882

Portrait and landscape painter; born in London; worked in London and Redhill, Surrey; died in Redhill.

316 The Harvest Cradle: noontide

A cornfield at harvest time; children play with a dog, left, while a mother covers her baby beneath a corn stook; in the distance the reapers and an extensive landscape view.

Panel 26 x 39 *ins.,* 66 x 99.1 *cms.*

Signed and dated, lower right: *J Linnell 1859.*

Probably painted on the edge of the North Downs, near Redhill. No sketch for no.316 exists in Linnell's *Liber Veritatis,* (the **MS.** illustrated list of the major part of his works, in a private collection), but there is a note to the effect that the painting, together with a companion piece *The Keg* (canvas 26 x 39 ins.), were painted in 1859 for the art dealer Fitzpatrick.

Prov.: Fitzpatrick, December, 1859, sold to John Heugh of Manchester; his sale Christie's, 28th April, 1860 (232), bought Flatow.

Lit.: A. J. Storey, *Life of John Linnell,* 1892, vol. 2, p. 275 (as *Cornfield Cradle*); *York Catalogue,* 1907, no. 28, illus. p. 18; *Preview,* 44, 1958, p. 424, illus.

Exh.: York, 1866 (251), lent Burton; Geneva, Musée d'Art, *Art et Travail,* 1957 (58).

Burton Bequest, 1882.   [*Plate 7*]

Gustave LOISEAU
1865 – 1935

Landscape painter; born in Paris; worked in Paris and Brittany, travelled in France.

934 Port-de-Goulphar, Belle-Ile-en-Mer

A sunlit headland jutting into the sea, viewed from higher ground; Port-de-Goulphar, a narrow inlet forming a natural harbour, is on the south side of Belle-Ile-en-Mer, off the coast of Brittany.

Canvas 24 x 32 *ins., 61 x 81.3 cms.*

Signed, lower left: *G. Loiseau*

Painted before 1900.

PROV.: The artist, 4th September, 1900, bought Durand-Ruel; Jean d'Alayer sale, Paris, 20th November, 1953 (86); Roland, Browse and Delbanco.

Purchased with a special grant from York City Council, 1959. [*Plate 28*]

LAURENCE STEPHEN LOWRY
1887 –

Painter of industrial urban life; born in Manchester; has worked in Manchester and Salford.

664 Clifford's Tower, York

Clifford's Tower, a medieval bastion on a grass mound, with the spire of St. Mary's, Castlegate, to the left.

Canvas 14 x 20 *ins., 35.6 x 50.8 cms.*

Signed and dated, lower left: *L. S. Lowry 1953*

LIT.: *Preview,* 22, 1953, illus. cover.

EXH.: Peterlee, Arts Council, *British Painters of Today,* 1955 (17).

Purchased as the Evelyn Award, 1953.

687 The Bandstand; Peel Park, Salford

An urban landscape with a park and bandstand in the middle distance; factories and industrial townscape beyond.

Canvas 17 x 24½ *ins., 43.2 x 62.2 cms.*

Signed and dated, lower left: *L. S. Lowry 1931*

Painted from a drawing, (dated 1925, Salford Art Gallery) made from a window of the Technical College in Salford. Lowry painted other versions of the subject: *The Park* (canvas 16 x 32 ins., dated 1946, Arts Council collection) shows a wider view, and *The Bandstand, Peel Park* (canvas 11½ x 15½ ins., dated 1928, Monks Hall Museum, Eccles) shows the bandstand to the left with figures in the foreground.

PROV.: The artist; Lefevre Gallery, 1943, bought Mrs. Grey.

LIT.: *Preview,* 34, 1956, p. 343, illus.

EXH.: N.E.A.C., 1941 (283); London, Lefevre Gallery, February-March, 1943 (19).

Presented by Mrs. C. Grey, 1953.

Nevil Oliver LUPTON
active 1827 – 1877

Landscape painter; worked in London and Hertfordshire.

135 A Lane in South Wales

In a wooded sunlit lane a man with a horse converses with a woman; a walled garden to the right.

Canvas 18 x 24 *ins., 45.7 x 61 cms.*

Signed and dated, lower left: *Nevil O. Lupton 1859.60.*

Lit.: *York Catalogue,* 1907, no. 16; *Preview,* 90, 1970, p. 817, illus.

Exh.: (possibly) R.A., 1860 (26), as *By the brook side—a scene in South Wales*; York, 1880 (230), lent Burton.

Burton Bequest, 1882.

Charles McCALL
1907 –

Painter of urban life; born in Edinburgh; has worked in Edinburgh and London, and travelled in Europe.

923 Pensive Woman

A woman seated on a bed, facing right; a boy's head on verso.

Hardboard 11¼ x 9¼ *ins., 28.6 x 23.5 cms.*

Signed and dated, upper left: *McCall 49*

Prov.: Leicester Galleries, 1950, bought Milner-White.

Exh.: London, Leicester Galleries, February, 1950 (2).

Presented by the Very Rev. E. Milner-White, 1958.

Horatio McCULLOCH
1805 – 1867

Landscape painter; born in Glasgow; worked in Glasgow and Edinburgh.

120 Kilchurn Castle, Loch Awe, Scotland

Three figures in the foreground by a loch; the castle with trees on a promontory, left.

Panel 9½ x 18½ *ins., 24.1 x 46.9 cms.*

Possibly a sketch for a larger picture; McCulloch painted the subject several times.

Lit.: *York Catalogue,* 1907, no. 40.

Burton Bequest, 1882.

Alexander MACKENZIE
1923 –

Abstract painter; born in Liverpool; has worked in Liverpool, St. Ives, Newlyn and Plymouth.

987 Three Blacks

Abstract composition of black rectangles against a grey and white background.

Hardboard 18 x 30 *ins., 45.7 x 76.2 cms.*

Signed, dated and inscribed, verso: *Three Blacks 1960/Alexander Mackenzie/Meadow Studio/Newlyn*

According to the artist, the composition was first inspired by an aerial view of the American coast.

PROV.: The artist, 1961, Waddington Galleries.

LIT.: *Preview,* 55, 1961, p. 527, illus.

EXH.: London, Waddington Galleries, *Mackenzie,* 1961 (4); Plymouth, City Art Gallery, *Mackenzie,* 1965 (20).

Presented by the Friends of York Art Gallery, 1961.

Paul MAITLAND
1863 – 1909

Painter of London views; born in Chelsea, London; worked and died in London.

35 Boats moored on the Thames

View along the Thames from Vestry wharves to Cheyne Walk and Lindsay House.

Panel 6¾ x 12 *ins., 17.1 x 30.5 cms.*

Signed, lower right: *P M*

A label on the reverse gives a date of c.1907, though this is inaccurate. Many such labels were apparently compiled by the family for his pictures and nearly all the dates are 1905 or later, although the stylistic differences of the paintings in question are considerable. It seems more likely that this picture was painted during the late 1880s.

PROV.: The artist's sisters, the Misses Maitland; the artist's cousins, Mr. and Mrs. Murray Urquhart, 1926; Leicester Galleries; Milner-White.

EXH.: London, Leicester Galleries, *Maitland,* 1928 (56), and 1948 (39).

Presented by the Very Rev. E. Milner-White through the York Civic Trust, 1949.

917 Thames—Steamboat Pier

View across the Thames; a woman on a bench and a gangway in the foreground; across the river a barge on the mudbank with Battersea warehouses and a factory chimney beyond.

Panel 8½ x 5¾ *ins.*, 21.6 x 14.6 *cms.*

Signed, lower left: *P. Maitland.*

Probably painted in the early 1880s, despite being labelled verso as c.1907 (see no. 35 above).

PROV.:   The artist's sisters, the Misses Maitland; the artist's cousins, Mr. and Mrs. Murray Urquhart, 1926; Leicester Galleries; Miss L. Browse, 1948; sold (through Roland, Browse and Delbanco) to Milner-White.

LIT.:   *Preview,* 43, 1958, p. 419, illus.

EXH.:   London, Leicester Galleries, *Maitland,* 1928 (60), and 1948 (3).

Presented by the Very Rev. E. Milner-White, 1958.

1037 Cheyne Walk in sunshine

A sunlit street on the embankment, with trees on the pavement.

Canvas 14 x 12 *ins.*, 35.6 x 30.5 *cms.*

Probably from the mid-1880s.

PROV.:   The artist's sisters, the Misses Maitland; the artist's cousins, Mr. and Mrs. Murray Urquhart, 1926; Leicester Galleries; Milner-White.

LIT.:   *Preview,* 63, 1963, p. 603, illus.

EXH.:   London, Leicester Galleries, Maitland, 1948 (49).

Presented by the Very Rev. E. Milner-White, 1963.   [*Plate 19*]

Ascribed to MAITLAND

574 The Thames above Battersea Bridge

A barge on the Thames, foreground, with factories in the background.

Canvas 10 x 8 *ins.*, 25.4 x 20.3 *cms.*

The coarser brush work and clumsy alteration in the background suggest that this is one of a number of works by a close friend and imitator of Maitland which passed into the latter's studio c.1907, and which after his death were mistakenly attributed to Maitland himself (information verbally from M. J. Franklin, 1971).

PROV.:   The artist's sisters, the Misses Maitland; the artist's cousins, Mr. and Mrs. Murray Urquhart, 1926; Leicester Galleries; Miss L. Browse 1948, sold Sotheby's, 18th April, 1951 (47).

LIT.:   *Preview,* 15, 1951, p. 176, illus.

EXH.:   London, Leicester Galleries, *Maitland,* 1928 (77), and 1948 (35); Dijon, 1957 (37).

Purchased, 1951.

Jacob MARIS
1837 – 1899

Landscape painter; born at The Hague; worked in The Hague, Antwerp and Paris; travelled in Germany and Switzerland; died in Karlsbad.

669   A Dutch Waterway

A wharf with moored boats and warehouses, left; the canal, centre, with a buoy in the foreground; to the right, a sailing barge with windmills in the distance.

Canvas 9⅛ x 14½ *ins.,* 23 x 36.9 *cms.*

Signed, lower right: *J Maris.*

Prov. :   Barbizon House; R.A. Peto, Bembridge; Marlborough Gallery, bought Milner-White.
Lit. :   *Preview,* 23, 1953, p. 247, illus.
Exh. :   London, Marlborough Gallery, June, 1951 (52).
Presented by the Very Rev. E. Milner-White, 1953.   [*Plate 13*]

Maxime-Émile-Louis MAUFRA
1861 – 1918

Painter of still life; born in Nantes; worked in Liverpool and in France, travelled in Scotland and Algeria; died at Ponce.

19   A Bouquet of Roses

A vase of roses on a patterned table cloth.

Canvas 20½ x 25½ *ins.,* 52.1 x 64.8 *cms.*

Signed and dated, lower right: *Maufra 1916*

Prov. :   The artist, 7th March, 1917, bought Durand-Ruel; sold 15th March, 1937; Mrs. Ackroyd; Sotheby's, 30th March, 1949 (128).
Lit. :   *Preview,* 7, 1949, pp. 76-77, illus.
Purchased, 1949.

Anton MAUVE
1838 – 1888

Landscape painter; born in Zaandam, Holland; worked in Haarlem, Oosterbeck, Amsterdam and The Hague; died in Arnhem.

562   On the Beach

Two horses pulling a cart across a flat beach; two figures in the sea on the left.

Canvas 12 x 18 *ins.,* 30.5 x 45.8 *cms.*

Signed, lower right: *A Mauve*

PROV.: Local collection; A. Coulter, York.

LIT.: *Preview*, 14, 1951, p. 159, illus.

Purchased, 1951. [*Plate 13*]

ROBERT MEDLEY
1905 –

Figurative and abstract painter; born in London; has worked in London and Paris.

640 Cyclists against a blue background

Three boys riding bicycles, left, watched by a mother with baby and a girl.

Canvas 61 x 53½ ins., 155 x 136 cms.

Signed and dated, lower right: *CRO.M. 2/51*

Commissioned by the Arts Council for the 1951 Festival of Britain. Two preliminary studies in black ink, body colour and oil (14 x 12 ins., and 13 x 11 ins.) are also in the Gallery's collection (presented by the Friends of York Art Gallery in 1965).

LIT.: *Preview*, 20, 1952, p. 225, illus. p. 223.

EXH.: London, Arts Council, *60 Paintings for '51*, 1951 (36); Durham University, *Medley*, 1953 (31); London, Whitechapel Art Gallery, *Medley*, 1963 (27); Liverpool, Walker Art Gallery, *Industry and the Artist*, 1965 (13).

Presented by the Arts Council, 1952.

GEORGES MICHEL
1763 – 1843

Landscape painter; born in Paris; worked in Paris and died there.

958 The Plain of St-Denis

A broad flat plain extending to white sky on the horizon with dark clouds above; a windmill and cottages appear in strong light in the right middle distance.

Paper on canvas 12¾ x 17¾ ins., 32.4 x 45.1 cms.

Stamped, verso: *G M*

Very probably the picture described by Sensier (see below) as in the collection of A. M. Féral in 1873.

PROV.: (A. M. Féral in 1873); American art market; Roland, Browse and Delbanco, 1958.

LIT.: A. Sensier, *Georges Michel*, Paris, 1873, p. 146 (42); *Preview*, 50, 1960, pp. 475-76, illus.

EXH.: London, Roland, Browse and Delbanco, April, 1958 (30).

Purchased, 1960. [*Plate 4*]

ALFRED MONTAGUE
active 1832–87

Marine painter; worked in England, Holland, France and Belgium; exhibited in London.

309   Coast Scene

A jetty with a round tower and a flag-pole, left; two women, one smoking a pipe, seated among kegs and creels in the foreground, with a fishing boat putting out in a rough sea, right.

Canvas 28 x 41½ *ins.,* 71.1 x 105.4 *cms.*

Signed and dated, lower right: *Alfred Montague 1854*

LIT.:   *York Catalogue,* 1907, no. 43.

EXH.:   (possibly) R.A., 1954 (596), as *Jetty on the Dutch Coast.*

Burton Bequest, 1882.

ADOLPHE-JOSEPH MONTICELLI
1824 – 1886

Painter of landscape and still life; born in Marseilles; worked in Marseilles and Paris; died in Marseilles.

575   Roses

Pink and white roses against a dark background.

Panel 8¼ x 11¾ *ins.,* 21 x 29.8 *cms.*

PROV.:   G. P. Dudley Wallis sale, Sotheby's, 18th April, 1951 (76).

LIT.:   *Preview,* 15, 1951, p. 171, illus., and 105, 1974, p. 942, illus.

Purchased, 1951.

ALBERT JOSEPH MOORE
1841 – 1893

Painter of decorative subjects; born in York; worked in York and London.

698   A Venus

Standing whole-length nude tying her hair with a ribbon; a long-necked white vase with blossom, right, and a blossoming tree in a blue and white jar in the background, right.

Canvas 63 x 30 *ins.,* 160 x 76.2 *cms.*

Signed with anthemion and dated *1869* in cartouche, upper left.

A preliminary oil study (canvas 17½ x 7½ *ins.,* signed and dated 1868) is in the collection of Mark Girouard; the figure is shown dressing or undressing, whereas in the finished painting the robe is eliminated.

No.698 develops a pose and composition found in *A Wardrobe* (canvas 39 x 19 ins.) painted in 1867 and now in Johannesburg (illus. Baldry, f.p. 34).

PROV.: The artist; F. R. Leyland sale, Christie's, 28th May, 1892 (36), bought Davis; Lady Astor; anon. sale Christie's, 12th May, 1922 (142), bought W. Sampson and Son; Cecil French.

LIT.: *Pall Mall Gazette,* 31st May, 1869; *The Art Journal,* 1869, p. 201; A. Baldry, *Albert Moore,* 1894, pp. 36-38, 103; *Preview,* 27, 1954, p. 282, illus., and 68, 1964, pp. 639-40; Q. Bell, *Victorian Artists,* 1967, p. 74, pl. 89; R. Spencer, *The Aesthetic Movement,* 1972, p. 42, illus. p. 38.

EXH.: R.A., 1869 (699); Harrogate, *The Nude in Victorian Art,* 1966 (71); Newcastle, Laing Art Gallery, *Albert Moore,* 1972 (24).

Cecil French Bequest, 1954.   [*Plate* 22]

699 End of a Sofa

Two sleeping female figures at either end of a sofa; two vases stand on the floor in the left foreground.

Card $9\frac{3}{4}$ x 15 *ins.,* 23.5 x 38.1 *cms.*

A sketch for *A Sofa* ($11\frac{1}{2}$ x 20 ins.) painted in 1875 and shown at the Grafton Gallery 1894, is in the collection of Mrs. B. Davis, the artist's great-niece (illus. Baldry, f.p. 76). There are slight differences in the pose and draperies, and the two prunus vases with flowering shrubs in the study are replaced by tapering jars with broad rims in the finished work.

Moore repeated the same composition with minor variations in the decorative details but different colour arrangements in two other finished works painted in 1875; *Apples* (canvas $11\frac{1}{2}$ x 20 ins.), now in the collection of Mrs. J. A. Newcomer, and *Beads* (canvas $11\frac{1}{4}$ x $19\frac{3}{4}$ ins.), now in the National Gallery of Scotland, Edinburgh (1019). Another related oil study, *Two Women on a Sofa* (canvas $11\frac{1}{2}$ x $20\frac{3}{4}$ ins.) is in the Handley-Read Collection.

PROV.: T. D. Harmson, sold Christie's, 5th October, 1951 (112; with two other items), bought Abbott; Cecil French.

EXH.: London, Leighton House, *High Victorian Art,* since 1969 (161); Newcastle, Laing Art Gallery, *Albert Moore,* 1972 (49), as *Colour Sketch for 'Apples'.*

Cecil French Bequest, 1954.

700 Kingcups

Two girls holding hands and jumping from a grass topped wall, left; a third stands below, seen from back.

Canvas $15\frac{1}{2}$ x $8\frac{1}{4}$ *ins.,* 39.4 x 21 *cms.*

Signed with anthemion on wall, left.

Painted in 1883.

Baldry states that the idea for the painting was based on an early work which had been brought to Moore by its owner in 1882 to retouch and sign. This may explain Moore's choice of a subject showing active physical movement—unusual in his works of this period. As was his usual practice for such subjects, Moore made his models repeat the jumping movement from a table in order to achieve realistic draperies. Baldry states that *Kingcups* was exhibited at McLean's Gallery in 1883, though the title does not appear in McLean's catalogue for this year; the picture is probably identifiable with *The Chase* which was no.118.

PROV.: Mrs. Brunner; Sir John Brunner; Arthur Jackson, Manchester, sold Christie's, 30th November, 1928 (80), bought Gooden and Fox; W. H. Woodward; Cecil French.

LIT.: A. L. Baldry, *Albert Moore*, 1894, pp. 54-55, 84, 104, illus. f.p. 88.

EXH.: London, McLean's Gallery, 1883 (118)?; York, *The Moore Family*, 1912 (139), lent Sir John Brunner; Newcastle, Laing Art Gallery, *Albert Moore*, 1972 (61).

Cecil French Bequest, 1954.

701　The Wardrobe Door

A standing draped young woman holding a wardrobe door, left.

Canvas 15½ x 6½ ins., 39.4 x 16.5 cms.

Signed with anthemion, below left.

Painted c. 1886.

A more detailed watercolour version entitled *Door of a Wardrobe* (15½ x 6½ ins.) was exhibited at the R.W.S., Winter, 1885-86 (172), and is in the collection of Terence Rowe; apart from differences in the colour scheme, it includes a Persian rug, foreground, a jar with foliage sprays on an ornate inlaid chest, right, and a decorative dado of arabesques on the wall behind the figure.

PROV.: The artist; W. Graham Robertson sale, Christie's, 22nd July, 1949 (144), as *The Painted Wardrobe*, bought David Gould; Cecil French.

LIT.: A. L. Baldry, *Albert Moore*, 1894, pp. 59, 105; *Preview*, 68, 1964, pp. 639-40, illus.

EXH.: Newcastle, Laing Art Gallery, *Albert Moore*, 1972 (65).

Cecil French Bequest, 1954.

HENRY MOORE
1831 – 1895

Landscape and marine painter; brother of Albert (q.v.); born in York; worked in York and London; died in Margate.

134　Gowbarrow Park, Ullswater

Cattle on a lake shore; high hills on the far shore.

Canvas 29½ x 43¼ ins., 75 x 109.9 cms.

Signed and inscribed, lower right: *H. Moore Gowborough . . .* and again: *Cattle and foreground repainted 1858 H.M.*

LIT.: *York Catalogue*, 1907, no. 6.

EXH.: R.A., 1854 (990), as *Study in Gowbarrow Park, Ullswater, Cumberland*; S.S., 1854 (175), as *Morning on Ullswater lake from Gowbarrow Park*; Liverpool, 1857 (204).

Burton Bequest, 1882.

137   Holne Bridge on the Dart, Devon

Three-arched stone bridge across a rocky stream with tree-covered banks.

Canvas 12 x 16 *ins.,* 30.5 x 40.7 *cms.*

Signed, dated and inscribed, lower right: *Holne Bridge/on the Dart, Devon/H. Moore. 1856*

See also no.249 below.

Bequeathed by Mrs. Hannah Deighton, 1913.

140   Landscape

Cattle drinking at a stream in a meadow; trees and a church spire in mid-distance.

Canvas 13 x 19 *ins.,* 33.1 x 48.3 *cms.*

Signed and dated, lower right: *H. Moore. 1857,* and signed on stretcher, verso, *H. Moore*

PROV.:   Unidentified sale, lot 257, 'Charming Landscape with Water and Cattle, a fine example H. Moore 1857' (label verso).

LIT.:   *York Catalogue,* 1907, no. 5.

EXH.:   York, *The Moore Family,* 1912 (145).

Burton Bequest, 1882.

220   Gwysaney Marshes

A sunlit meadow with a stunted oak and cattle.

Canvas 16½ x 26 *ins.,* 42 x 66.5 *cms.*

Signed, lower left: *H Moore*

PROV.:   Anon. sale, Christie's, 20th April, 1925 (83), bought Langley Brown.

Presented by H. K. Henderson, 1948.

249   On the Dart, Devon

Three-arched stone bridge, centre, over a woody stream with hay cart crossing; a cowgirl with three cows in the foreground.

Canvas 13 x 20 *ins.,* 33.1 x 50.8 *cms.*

Signed and dated, lower left: *H M* (monogram) *1866,* and signed and dated on stretcher verso, *On the Dart/St Devon/H. Moore,* and *H. Moore 1862* (sic).

The same view as in no.137 above, painted a little further downstream.

LIT.:   *York Catalogue,* 1907, no. 1, illus. p. 8.

Burton Bequest, 1882.

253   In Richmond Park

Two cows under a broad tree, centre, with cattle beneath trees, left background; flat landscape with pool and distant buildings, right.

Canvas 15½ x 26¼ ins., 38.1 x 66.7 cms.

Signed and dated, lower right: *H Moore 1856.*, and inscribed with title on stretcher, verso.

PROV.:   Thomas Walker, York.
Presented by Thomas Walker, 1912.

318   Crossing the Bar

Grey sea and sky, with a sailing ship, centre, and a steamer in the right distance.

Canvas 34½ x 64 ins., 81.7 x 163 cms.

Signed and dated, lower right: *H. Moore. 1873-4*

A letter, verso, from Moore states: '*Crossing the Bar* was exhibited in the R.A. in 1873 and the reason it has a second date is that in 1874 I did a week's work upon it as I was not quite satisfied with it as it appeared in the R.A. ....'.

PROV.:   The artist; McClean, London; Alfred Hunt; F. H. Gossage, sold Brown and Rose, 18th February, 1908 (31) anon. purchaser; anon. sale, Christie's, 18th March, 1911 (90), bought Spielmann.
LIT.:   *The Art Journal*, 1873, p. 236, and 1874, p. 334.
EXH.:   R.A., 1873 (641); Liverpool, 1874 (311); York, *The Moore Family*, 1912 (152), lent anonymously, and *York Artists*, 1914 (240).
Purchased by public subscription, 1912.   [*Plate 14*]

344   Evening: Cottages   on   the   braeside   near   Castletown,   Braemar, Aberdeenshire

Thatched cottages and a peat stack, centre, with cattle standing in a foreground stream; to the right, a view down on to a broad river valley with mountains in the evening sun beyond.

Canvas 26 x 48 ins., 66.1 x 122 cms.

Signed and dated, lower left: *H Moore 1860.*

A label, verso, in the artist's own hand reads 'Painted on the spot'.

LIT.:   *York Catalogue*, 1907, no. 3.
EXH.:   S.S., 1853 (453).
Burton Bequest, 1882.

352   Calm before a storm

To the right, a fishing boat on a calm sea, with two others in distance left; a stormy sky above.

Canvas 48 x 72 ins., 122 x 183 cms.

Signed, lower left: *H. Moore*

Painted in or before 1883; a study for this picture was made between five and nine a.m. off the east end of the Isle of Wight, possibly that now in the collection of Mrs. B. Davis, the artist's grand-daughter.

PROV.: The artist; his daughter Mrs. Bogle.

LIT.: *The Art Journal,* 1883, pp. 253, 341; *The Magazine of Art,* 1893-94, p. 384; F. Maclean, *Henry Moore,* 1905, pp. 78-9, 199, illus. f.p. 96.

EXH.: R.A., 1883 (1444); Manchester, City Art Gallery, 1883 (94); York, 1884 (291); Manchester, Jubilee Exhibition, 1887 (126); Paris, Salon, 1894; London, Earl's Court, 1897 (26), lent Miss Moore (later Mrs. Bogle); York, *The Moore Family,* 1912 (180).

Presented by Mrs. Linton Bogle, 1915.

452 Hob Moor (I)

Rustic bridge across a wooded stream, foreground, with cattle in a meadow beyond; church spire and buildings background right; Hob Moor, of which little more than a few fields now remain, lay between the villages of Acomb and Dringhouses on the outskirts of York.

Panel 9 x 6 ins., 22.6 x 15.2 cms.

PROV.: T. Penrose, York; Burton.

LIT.: *York Catalogue,* 1907, no. 2.

EXH.: York, 1866 (147), as *Small Landscape,* lent Penrose.

Burton Bequest, 1882.

453 Hob Moor (II)

Two sheep in a wood; see no. 452 above.

Panel 9 x 6 ins., 22.6 x 15.2 cms.

PROV.: T. Penrose, York; Burton.

LIT.: *York Catalogue,* 1907, no. 4.

EXH.: York, 1866 (149), as *Small landscape,* lent Penrose.

Burton Bequest, 1882.

1013 Italian Shepherdess on the Corniche near Nice

A little girl with headscarf sitting on rocks by a coast road while her laden white horse feeds from a nose basket.

Canvas 15¾ x 24 ins., 40 x 61 cms.

Signed and dated, lower left: *H. Moore 1858-9* and on label, verso: *An Italian Shepherdess/on the Cornice Road/near Nice—Painted on the spot/ Henry Moore/1858*

PROV.: H. J. Ware, by descent.

EXH.: York, 1866 (134), and 1879 (309), on both occasions lent H. J. Ware.

Presented by Col. N. Innes Ware, 1962.

attributed to François-Henri MULARD
1769 – 1850

Portrait painter; born, worked and died in Paris, travelled in Italy.

443 Portrait of a Gentleman

Head and shoulders of a dark-haired young man in a high white stock and dark coat looking right.

Canvas 24½ x 20 *ins.*, 62.2 x 50.8 *cms.*

Acquired in 1949 as an English portrait by an unknown artist. An old label, verso, had led to a belief that it was by H. R. Morland (1730-97) but it would seem very probable that the label was inscribed *H. Mulard* and then misread. The portrait is clearly French, early 19th-century, and within the wider circle of J. L. David; an attribution to Mulard is therefore probable.

LIT.: *Preview*, 10, 1950, illus. cover.

Presented by Hugh Agnew, 1949.

Sir David MURRAY
1849 – 1933

Landscape painter; born in Glasgow; worked in Glasgow and London, where he died.

195 Landscape

Cattle and sheep resting beneath trees; a hedge, right, and a rough track, centre.

Canvas 24 x 36 *ins.*, 61 x 91.5 *cms.*

Signed and dated, lower right: *David Murray 1893*

Presented by J. E. Champney, 1929.

198 Autumn: the waning year

Cows in a foreground meadow; to the right, a lane with two figures and a horse; to the left, a stream with a figure on a bridge; cottages and autumnal trees in the background.

Canvas 24 x 36 *ins.*, 61 x 91.5 *cms.*

Signed, lower right: *David Murray*

EXH.: Liverpool, 1906 (209).

Presented by Sir Edwin Cooper, R.A., the artist's executor, 1939.

Paul NASH
1889 – 1946

Painter of landscape and imaginative subjects; born in London; worked in London, on the Kent and Sussex coast and in Oxford; died in Boscombe.

868 Winter Sea

A formalised composition of grey waves beneath a wintry sky with a setting sun.

Canvas 28 x 38 *ins., 71.2 x 96.6 cms.*

Signed and dated, lower left: *Paul Nash 1925/37*

The painting is in a fragile condition; the top paint layer is loosening away from an original paint layer, a consequence of the painting having taken twelve years (1925/37) to complete.

The *Winter Sea* represents the culmination of many studies by Nash of the sea breaking on the flat Kent coast at Dymchurch, on the edge of Romney Marsh. Having visited there in 1919 and 1920, Nash rented a cottage at Dymchurch between 1921 and 1924. Pencil and watercolour studies of this subject dating from 1921-24 (illus. Eates, pls. 32-35, 38-41a) show Nash moving towards the formalised York composition, described by Margot Eates as 'one of the greatest achievements of the English school'. An almost exact sketch for 968, in conté and watercolour (14¾ x 21 ins.), is in the Graves Art Gallery, Sheffield.

PROV.:   The artist, 1937-38, bought Mrs. Grey.

LIT.:   H. Read, *Paul Nash*, Harmondsworth, 1944, pl. 9; M. Eates (ed.), *Paul Nash*, 1948, pp. 3, 27, pl. 28; A. Bertram, *Paul Nash*, 1955, pp. 139-40, 305n; J. Rothenstein, *Modern English Painters*, vol. 2, 1956, p. 108, pl. 9; *Preview*, 34, 1956, pp. 343-45, illus., and 52, 1960, pp. 500, 502-03, illus.; D. Anderson, *Elements of Design*, New York, 1961, pp. 105, 118, illus.; J. Rothenstein, *Paul Nash*, 1961, pl. IV; J. Bradshaw, 'Paul Nash', *Leeds Art Calendar*, 49, 1962, pp. 14-15; M. Eates, *Paul Nash*, 1973, pp. 32, 120, 129, pl. 40.

EXH.:   Pittsburgh, Carnegie Institute, *International Exhibition*, 1937 (121), as *Dark Sea at Dymchurch;* London, Leicester Galleries, *Paul Nash*, 1938 (34); National Gallery, *British Painting*, 1940 (176); Leeds, *Nash-Hepworth*, 1943 (21); London, Tate Gallery, *Nash*, 1948 (10); Arts Council, *British Painting 1925-50*, 1951 (48); New York, St. Louis, San Francisco, British Council, *British Painting*, 1956-57 (58), Moscow and Leningrad, *British Painting*, 1960 (104).

Presented by Mrs. C. Grey, 1956.   [*Plate 40*]

ALGERNON NEWTON
1880 – 1968

Painter of landscape and urban scenes; born in Hampstead, London; worked in London, Cornwall and Yorkshire.

27 In Kensington

A view down a deserted, sunlit suburban street with a garden wall to the left, and regency houses to the right.

Canvas 18 x 24 *ins., 45.8 x 61 cms.*

PROV.:   Sir Phillip Sassoon, presented to the C.A.S., 1923.

LIT.:   *The Studio*, 92, 1926, p. 235, illus. p. 232.

EXH.:   London, Tate Gallery, *C.A.S. 25th Anniversary*, 1935 (43).

Presented by the Contemporary Art Society, 1928.

William W. NICOL
active 1848 – 1864

Painter of domestic genre; worked in Worcester, Cheltenham and London.

180   Quiet

A domestic interior with a woman seated on a sofa reading to a child beside her.

Canvas 18 x 15¼ *ins.,* 45.7 x 38.7 *cms.*

Signed, dated and inscribed, lower right: *M.N. et M.W.J.N. 1860 W.W.N. W. W. Nicol pinxit.*

The inscription suggests that the picture shows Nicol's wife and child.

Lit.:   *York Catalogue,* 1907, no. 79; C. Wood, *Dictionary of Victorian Painters,* 1971, p. 112, illus. p. 337.

Exh.:   York, 1879 (128), lent Burton.

Burton Bequest, 1882.

Roderic O'CONOR
1860 – 1940

Figurative painter; born in Roscommon, Ireland; worked in London, Antwerp, Paris and Brittany; died in Neuil-sur-Layon.

961   Self Portrait

Sombre head and shoulders portrait of the artist in overcoat, scarf and top hat, facing left.

Canvas 24 x 19½ *ins.,* 61 x 49.6 *cms.*

Inscribed, upper left: *'A l'ami O'Conor'* (?)

Possibly painted c.1910. The inscription is almost indecipherable but the suggested text seems the most probable: the picture was acquired by Manteau from 'the friend of O'Conor' (letter from Victor Waddington in Gallery files dated 9th April, 1964). The features agree well enough with a photograph of O'Conor and another *Self Portrait* (with Alden Brooks in 1960). Clive Bell described O'Conor in Paris, c.1900, as 'a swarthy man, with a black moustache, greying when I met him, tallish and sturdy. He carried a stick and there was nothing Bohemian about his appearance'.

Prov.:   'a friend of O'Conor'; Manteau Gallery, Paris; Waddington Galleries.

Lit.:   *Preview,* 50, 1960, pp. 477-78, illus.; D. Sutton, 'Roderic O'Conor', *The Studio,* 160, November, 1960, pp. 194-95; *Preview,* 67, 1964, p. 635.

Purchased, 1960.

1095 The Wave

Wide seascape with a wave breaking across the foreground.

Canvas 28½ x 36 *ins., 72.4 x 91.5 cms.*

Signed and dated, lower left: *O'Conor 1898*

PROV.: Vente O'Conor, Paris, 7th February, 1956, bought Roland, Browse and Delbanco; Mrs. J. Weir; Roland, Browse and Delbanco.

LIT.: *Preview,* 67, 1964, pp. 632-33, illus.; *Burl. Mag.,* CXII, July, 1971, p. 420.

EXH.: London, Roland, Browse and Delbanco, March-April, 1957 (15), April-May, 1964 (17), and June, 1971 (22).

Purchased with the aid of a grant from the Victoria and Albert Museum, 1964.

[*Plate 29*]

AMEDÉE OZENFANT
1886 – 1966

Painter of still life; born in St-Quentin; worked in Paris, London and New York; died in Cannes.

891 Still life with jug

Still life with jug, bottle and architectural features.

Gouache on blue paper 14½ x 11 *ins., 37.4 x 28.2 cms.*

Signed, dated and inscribed, bottom right: *Cruche et architecture/O 1925.*

PROV.: Bellier sale, Paris, December, 1956; Roland, Browse and Delbanco.

LIT.: *Preview,* 38, 1957, pp. 373-74, illus., and 52, 1960, p. 500.

Purchased, 1957. [*Plate 37*]

JOHN PARTRIDGE
1790 – 1872

Portrait painter; born in Glasgow; worked in London; travelled in Italy 1823-27; died in London.

1125 The Clough-Taylor Family

Five half-length figures; Mrs. Emma Clough-Taylor (d. 1885) seated centre, with her arm around her eldest son Edward (1822-92), who stands on the left, her other arm resting on her daughter seated at her feet; her husband Edward Clough-Taylor (1786-1851) behind her with their second son to the right.

Canvas 51 x 61½ *ins., 129.5 x 156.2 cms.*

No.1125 appears in Partridge's *Sitter Book* (MS. in National Portrait Gallery archive) as item 14 in 1830: 'Edward Clough Taylor and his family ½ length £210'. The family lived at Kirkham Abbey and, later, at Firby Hall, near Kirkham.

PROV.: Edward Clough-Taylor, by descent.

Presented by Lt. Col. W. Clough-Taylor, 1966.

A. PASCITTI
active 1873

Probably the Antonio Pascitti active in Trieste in the 19th century.

277 The Duet

Five women relaxing on a bank by a stream; one plays a guitar while another sings.

Canvas 14¼ x 18¼ *ins.,* 36.2 x 46.4 *cms.*

Signed and dated, lower right: *A. Pascitti 1873.*

LIT.: *York Catalogue,* 1907, no. 89.

EXH.: (possibly) Continental Galleries, 1879 (194), as *The Musical Party.*

Burton Bequest, 1882.

DANIEL PASMORE

Both father (active 1829-65) and son (active 1829-91) were called Daniel, and their work is at present indistinguishable; narrative and history painters; worked in London.

131 The Letter Carrier

A woman stands in the entrance to a house with a child and dog beside her, waiting for a postman to sort letters.

Canvas 18¼ x 14¼ *ins.,* 46.2 x 36.2 *cms.*

Signed and dated, lower left: *D Pasmore/1862*

LIT.: *York Catalogue,* 1907, no. 101.

Burton Bequest, 1882.

269 Doorway, Haddon Hall

In a doorway, a seated young man looks up at a young girl standing by him; 17th-century costumes.

Canvas 35½ x 27½ *ins.,* 90.2 x 69.9 *cms.*

Signed and dated, lower right: *D. Pasmore 1860*

Haddon Hall in Derbyshire, the home of the Vernon and Manners families, was frequently painted in the 19th century (see also Horsley, no. 494); as Martindale Hall the house was used by Walter Scott in *Peveril of the Peak*, 1822. The doorway shown in no.269 was the one through which Dorothy Vernon is popularly supposed to have escaped to her lover, John Manners, in 1567.

LIT.: *York Catalogue,* 1907, no. 110.

Burton Bequest, 1882.

284 Courting at the Well

Sailor with a hat and knapsack leaning on a well from which a girl draws water; an overgrown doorway beyond, with a boy peeping through.

Canvas 18 x 14 *ins., 45.7 x 35.6 cms.*

Signed and dated, lower right: *D Pasmore 1862*

Shown at York in 1883 as *Popping the Question.*

LIT.:   *York Catalogue,* 1907, no. 65.

Burton Bequest, 1882.

493 The Cavalier's Refreshment

Interior with a cavalier, right, holding a musket in one hand, the other resting on his powder pouch; behind him a serving maid with a tray bearing flagon and glasses; a table, left, with muskets, flagons, jackets and boots.

Canvas 14 x 20 *ins., 35.6 x 50.8 cms.*

Signed and dated, lower right: *D Pasmore 1860*

LIT.:   *The Art Journal,* 1860, p. 144; *York Catalogue,* 1907, no. 106.

EXH.:   S.S., 1860 (311), as *Preparing for a change.*

Burton Bequest, 1882.

VICTOR PASMORE
1908 –

Figurative and abstract painter; born in Chelsham, Surrey; has worked in London, Newcastle and Malta.

573 Café Interior

Seated and standing figures in a café interior, with a waitress behind a glass partition in the background.

Canvas mounted on millboard 29⅜ x 18¾ *ins., 75.6 x 47.6 cms.*

Signed, lower right: *V P*

Painted in 1946. The picture has been cut down from a larger composition.

PROV.:   The artist, 1950, bought Roland, Browse and Delbanco.

LIT.:   A. Bowness, 'The Paintings and Constructions of Victor Pasmore', *Burl. Mag.,* CII, May, 1960, p. 201n.

EXH.:   London, Roland, Browse and Delbanco, April-June, 1951 (22), as *The Café;* Dijon, 1957 (44); Tate Gallery, *C.A.S. 50th Anniversary,* 1960 (55), and *Pasmore,* May-June, 1965 (54); Arts Council, *Decade 1940-50,* 1972-73 (40).

Purchased with the aid of a grant from the Contemporary Art Society, 1951.

Luigi PERICLE (Giovanetti)
1916 –

Abstract painter; born in North Italy; has worked in Switzerland.

1060 Supramental Transformation

Dark abstract composition built of compact squares.

Canvas 25 x 20 *ins.,* 63.5 x 50.8 *cms.*

Signed and dated, verso: *Luigi Pericle 1962/3*

LIT.:   *Preview,* 65, 1964, pp. 615, 617, illus.
EXH.:   York, *Pericle,* 1965 (55).
Purchased, 1963.

1061 March of Time I

Black calligraphic shapes against a light, textured background.

Canvas 20 x 25 *ins.,* 50.8 x 63.5 *cms.*

Signed and dated, verso: *Luigi Pericle 1962/3*

LIT.:   *Preview,* 65, 1964, pp. 616-17, illus.
EXH.:   York, *Pericle,* 1965 (54).
Purchased with the aid of an anonymous donation through the York Civic Trust, 1964.

Charles PETTITT
1831 – 1885

Landscape painter; born in Birmingham, son of Joseph Paul (q.v.); worked in London, travelled in England and Norway.

296 Lyster Fjord, Norway

A fjord in a mountainous landscape; a boat by a landing stage in the foreground; a lakeside village to the left, and paddle steamers and boats to the right.

Canvas 23¾ x 36 *ins.,* 60.3 x 91.4 *cms.*

Signed and dated, lower left: *18 CP* (monogram) *74,* and signed, dated and inscribed, verso: *Lyster (& Dosen) on/the Lyster-Fjord: /Sogn-Fjord/ Norway/Charles Pettitt 1874*

In poor condition.

PROV.:   G. Strickland, London; Rawdon.
LIT.:   *York Catalogue,* 1907, no. 27; C. Wood, *Dictionary of Victorian Painters,* 1971, p. 124.
EXH.:   York, 1880 (1207), 1881 (70), and 1882 (608), on each occasion lent Strickland.
Rawdon Bequest, 1895.

Joseph Paul PETTITT
1812 – 1882

History painter; born in Birmingham, father of Charles (q.v.); worked in London and Birmingham, where he died.

1118 Armageddon

A vast Biblical scene of destruction; falling masonry and statue in the left foreground; figures taking refuge from a stormy sea on a rocky plateau, centre; crumbling cities on hill tops beyond, with erupting mountains in the background. The scene illustrates Revelations XVI, verses 17-19, describing the Apocalyptic vision of St. John in which the city of Armageddon is destroyed by the wrath of God.

Canvas 53 x 102 *ins., 134.6 x 259.8 cms.*

Signed and dated, lower left: *J. P. Pettitt 1852*

PROV.: John Duckett, Sevenoaks; Agnew.

LIT.: *Preview,* 72, 1965, pp. 674-76, illus.

EXH.: Birmingham, Society of Artists, 1852 (252); S.S., 1853 (428); London, Agnews, July-August, 1965 (9).

Purchased, 1965.

John PHILLIP
1816 – 1867

Portrait and genre painter; born in Aberdeen; worked in Aberdeen and London, travelled in Spain and Italy.

384 Collecting the Offering in a Scottish Kirk

The elder in a tartan plaid, left, passing the collecting box to five adults and two children in a pew; in the background the minister in his pulpit with the congregation singing below.

Canvas 32 x 45½ *ins., 81.3 x 115.6 cms.*

Signed and dated, lower left: *J P* (monogram) *55*

Relined 1969.

The figures in the foreground are apparently members of the Murray family; the kirk interior is that of Alford, West Aberdeenshire, where Phillip stayed during the summer of 1855; the square or 'pumphel' pew in the foreground is the family pew of the local squire.

A finished sketch for no. 384 belonging to the Scottish sculptor William Brodie (1815-1881) was exhibited at the R.S.A. in 1868, no. 584, and 1880, no. 204.

PROV.: W. Wells of Redleaf, Kent, sale Christie's, 27th April, 1860 (93), bought Gambart; Henry Woodhouse sale, Christie's, 19th May, 1866 (129), bought Burton.

LIT.:   *The Art Journal*, 1855, p. 175, and 1867, p. 127; J. Dafforne, *Pictures by John Phillip R.A.*, [1877], p. 27; *York Catalogue*, 1907, no. 32, illus. p. 21; *Preview*, 76, 1966, p. 706, illus.

EXH.:   R.A., 1855 (298), with subtitle *Give and ye shall receive;* Leeds, *National Exhibition*, 1868 (1152); Glasgow, 1911 (157); London, Whitechapel Art Gallery, 1912 (25); Aberdeen, *Phillip*, 1967 (29); R.A., 1969 (206).

Burton Bequest, 1882.   [*Plate 8*]

FREDERICK RICHARD PICKERSGILL
1820 – 1900

Portrait and genre painter; born and worked in London; died in the Isle of Wight.

285 The Mountain Spring

A woman with a child filling a jug from a stream.

Panel 21¾ x 16¼ *ins.*, 55.2 x 41.3 *cms.*

Signed and dated, lower right: *F. R. Pickersgill A.R.A. 1850*

According to a letter from the artist, on the verso, dated 14th January, 1855, the subject was based on an incident he saw in north Wales.

LIT.:   *York Catalogue*, 1907, no. 5.

EXH.:   York, 1866 (135), lent Burton.

Burton Bequest, 1882.

JOHN PIPER
1903 –

Landscape and decorative artist; born at Epsom, Surrey; has worked principally in London and Kent.

582 Stair Hole, Lulworth

Lulworth, on the Dorset coast, near Weymouth; a narrow cove with sharply rising cliffs and a waterfall in the background.

Canvas 20 x 24 *ins.*, 50.8 x 61 *cms.*

Signed, lower right: *John Piper*

Painted in 1948.

PROV.: Leicester Galleries 1948; Howard Bliss; Leicester Galleries; Milner-White.

EXH.:   London, Leicester Galleries, December, 1948 (27), and *Bliss Collection*, 1950 (108); Dijon, 1957 (44).

Presented by the Very Rev. E. Milner-White, 1951.   [*Plate 43*]

Russell PLATT
1920 –

Figurative painter; born in Wallasey; has worked in London, Kent and York.

878 York Minster (Cathedral 5)

A composition deriving from the west front of York Minster covered with scaffolding.

Hardboard 24 x 32 *ins.*, 61 x 81.3 *cms.*

Painted in 1956.

LIT.: *Preview*, 37, 1957, pp. 367-68, illus.

EXH.: York, *Three Modern Artists*, 1956 (45).

Purchased as the Evelyn Award, 1956.

Frank Huddlestone POTTER
1845 – 1887

Painter of domestic genre; born in London; worked in London and Antwerp.

715 Young girl reading,

A young girl standing in a long, dark dress facing right and reading a book.

Canvas 28 x 11½ *ins.*, 71.2 x 29.2 *cms.*

Painted c.1880.

PROV.: Anon. sale, Christie's, 7th May, 1954 (143), bought Roland, Browse and Delbanco.

LIT.: *Preview*, 36, 1956, p. 363, illus.

EXH.: Dijon, 1957 (32).

Purchased, 1954.

James Ferrier PRYDE
1866 – 1941

Narrative painter; born in Edinburgh; worked in Paris and London where he died.

7 The Untouchables

A sombre picture of ten beggars standing before a flat landscape; painted throughout in greys and black. Pryde's title would suggest the figures are outcasts.

Canvas 36 x 43½ *ins.*, 91.5 x 110.5 *cms.*

Painted c.1929-40.

The Untouchables and another picture *The Death of the Great Bed* were worked on for some twelve years and left unfinished at Pryde's death. A squared up study for no. 7 (oil on paper laid down on canvas 36 x 42 ins., Pryde sale, lot 55) is now in the collection of L. S. Michael. *The Untouchables* also appears in the background of a picture by James Gunn (1893-1964) entitled *A Souvenir of James Pryde*, painted shortly after Pryde's death. A preliminary version of the composition, showing only five figures (canvas 37 x 44 ins.) was sold at Christie's, 13th July, 1973, lot 300 (the sale catalogue stated it had been lot 57 in the Pryde sale, but it must have been lot 56, *Itinerant Players*).

PROV.: Mrs. James Pryde sale, Christie's, 2nd July, 1948 (57).

LIT.: *Preview*, 5, 1949, p. 51, illus.; D. Hudson, *James Pryde*, 1949, p. 81.

EXH.: Edinburgh, Arts Council, *Pryde*, 1949 (15).

Presented by the Very Rev. E. Milner-White, through the York Civic Trust, 1948.

JAMES BAKER PYNE
1800 – 1870

Landscape and marine painter; born in Bristol; worked in Bristol and London, travelled in Europe; died in London.

256 Scene on the Rhine

An extensive view over a wide river with rocky shores, a ruined castle and distant spires in the right mid-distance; on a ledge in the foreground some figures working.

Canvas 22¾ x 30 ins., 58 x 76.2 cms.

Signed indistinctly, lower centre left: *JBP . . .*

Overcleaned.

Possibly showing the ruined monastery of St. Goar and the town of Goarhausen, the subject of a watercolour by Pyne dated 1861, no. 572 in his *Memoranda*. Although an oil of this subject does not appear in the *Memoranda*, no.256 is stylistically attributable to Pyne and has traditionally been given to him.

LIT.: *York Catalogue*, 1907, no. 29, as unknown artist.

Burton Bequest, 1882.

275 Venice with the Strada Ferrata from the Lagunes

Sailing barges and gondolas in the centre foreground, a railway viaduct with a train to the right.

Canvas 14 x 25¾ ins., 35.6 x 65.4 cms.

Signed, dated and numbered, lower right: *J B Pyne 1855 N°. 393*, and signed, dated, numbered and inscribed with title, verso.

A small area of flaking, bottom left, repaired in 1973.

No.393 in Pyne's *Memoranda;* painted in September 1854, retouched in March 1855 and varnished in May the same year, when it was purchased by Agnews; turpentine and mastic varnish were used for the medium.

PROV.: May, 1855, bought Agnews; December, 1856, bought J. Barker; Joseph Craven sale, Christie's, 27th March, 1874 (161), bought Burton.

LIT.: J. B. Pyne, *Picture Memoranda* (MS. in the Victoria and Albert Museum), vol. 2; *York Catalogue,* 1907, no. 10; *Preview,* 44, 1958, p. 425, illus.

Burton Bequest, 1882. [*Plate 12*]

1230 View across the Avon

View across a wide valley; four figures and a donkey in the foreground; village with a factory kiln in the middle distance and hills in the far distance.

Canvas 17 x 25 *ins., 43 x 63.5 cms.*

Signed, lower right: *J. B. Pyne*

Presumably painted before 1832-33 when Pyne left Bristol.

Presented by the family of J. B. Morrell, 1963.

GERMAIN RIBOT
active 1870 died 1893

Painter of still life; son of Théodule-Augustin (q.v.); worked in Paris.

682 Kitchen Boys

An interior with two kitchen boys in white with white hats by a large chopping table; through a doorway, left, two more boys with a tray and a basket.

Canvas 9½ x 12½ *ins., 24.2 x 31.8 cms.*

Signed, lower left: *G. Ribot*

Until now attributed to Ribot *père.* The signature was first correctly read by M. André Watteau (letter in Gallery files dated 10th July, 1973).

PROV.: Anon. sale, Sotheby's, 29th July, 1953 (89).

LIT.: *Preview,* 24, 1953, p. 258, illus., as T-A. Ribot.

Purchased, 1953.

THÉODULE-AUGUSTIN RIBOT
1823 – 1891

Painter of still life; born at St-Nicolas d'Attez; worked in Paris; travelled in Germany; died at Colombes.

20 Still life with jug

A two-handled metal vase with lid, a jug and an apple.

Canvas 21¾ x 18¼ *ins., 55.3 x 46.4 cms.*

Signed, lower left: *A Ribot*

Painted c.1880.

PROV.: J. M. Cargher, London, sold Christie's, 3rd December, 1948 (28), bought Roland, Browse and Delbanco.

LIT.: *Preview,* 7, 1949, pp. 77-78, illus.

Purchased, 1949.   [*Plate 17*]

441 Still life with oysters

Oyster shells on a table, those in the foreground open.

Canvas 9½ x 12¾ ins., 24.2 x 32.4 cms.

Possibly identifiable as *Oysters* by Ribot exhibited at the Goupil Gallery, London, Spring 1922, no.74. The painting was at one time attributed to Manet. A closely related composition by Ribot, *Oysters and Mussels* (10 x 13 ins.) was exhibited at the Arcade Gallery, London, in March, 1965, no.2.

PROV.: Leopold Megret; Beaux Arts Gallery, London.

LIT.: *Preview,* 12, 1950, p. 137, illus.

EXH.: London, Beaux Arts Gallery, April, 1950 (38).

Purchased, 1950.

JEAN-PAUL RIOPELLE
1923 –

Abstract painter; born in Montreal; has worked in Montreal and Paris.

942 La Vallée

An abstract composition in thickly impasted greens, maroons and whites with a grey interval, centre.

Canvas 22½ x 30 ins., 57.2 x 76.2 cms.

Signed, lower right: *riopelle*

Painted in 1957.

PROV.: Tooth's, 1957, bought by the C.A.S.

LIT.: *Preview,* 47/48, 1959, pp. 448-50, illus.

EXH.: London, Tooth's, October/November, 1957 (9); Arts Council, *C.A.S. Recent Acquisitions,* 1959 (52); Tate Gallery, *C.A.S. 50th Anniversary,* 1960 (160); Manchester, Institute of Contemporary Arts, *Canadian Trio,* 1961 (31).

Presented by the Contemporary Art Society, 1959.

WILLEM ROELOFS
1822 – 1897

Landscape painter; born in Amsterdam; worked in Utrecht, The Hague and Brussels; died at Berchem near Antwerp.

928 Dragging Peat

Flat open landscape beneath a cloudy sky with a view across a stretch of water; a punt and two men, centre, with trees and a windmill beyond.

Canvas on panel 11⅛ x 17¾ *ins.*, 28.2 x 45.1 *cms.*

Signed and numbered, lower right: *W. Roelofs. 159'* and lower left: *R.62.;* inscribed, verso *159 Etang et Tireurs de Tourbe à Noorden*

Noorden is presumably the Norden on the north-west coast of Germany, very near the Dutch border.

PROV.:   A. Coulter, York.
LIT.:   *Preview,* 44, 1958, pp. 422-23, illus.
Purchased, 1958.

LEONARD ROSOMAN
1913 –

Figurative painter; born in London; has worked in London and Edinburgh.

716   Trees against pale sunlight

Four trees against a pale, misty sunlight.

Canvas 36 x 28 *ins.,* 91.5 x 71.1 *cms.*

Signed lower left: *Leonard Rosoman*

Painted c.1952.

PROV.:   Roland, Browse and Delbanco.
LIT.:   *Preview,* 34, 1956, p. 346, illus.
EXH.:   London, Roland, Browse, and Delbanco, May-June, 1954 (14); Dijon, 1957 (46); Edinburgh, Society of Scottish Artists, 1959 (9).
Purchased, 1954.

872   Taverna la Fenice, Venice, No. 2

The interior of a Venetian café with plants.

Canvas 18 x 24 *ins.,* 45.7 x 61 *cms.*

Signed, lower left: *Leonard Rosoman*

Painted in 1952-53. A companion picture, *Taverna la Fenice, No. 1,* is in a private collection.

PROV.:   Roland, Browse and Delbanco, 1954, bought by the C.A.S.
LIT.:   *Preview,* 37, 1957, p. 369, illus.
EXH.:   London, Roland, Browse and Delbanco, May-June, 1954 (19); Edinburgh, Society of Scottish Artists, 1959 (8).
Presented by the Contemporary Art Society, 1956.

PIERRE-ÉTIENNE-THÉODORE ROUSSEAU
1812 – 1867

Landscape painter; born in Paris; worked in Paris and Fontainebleau; died in Barbizon.

914 Landscape with red sunset

A vivid red sunset seen past a tree, left, a small pond and distant low mountains.

Panel 12 x 18 *ins.,* 30.5 x 45.8 *cms.*

Signed, lower left: *TH.R.*

Robert L. Herbert (letter in Gallery files dated 20th December, 1967), judging from a photograph, suggested a date in the early 1850s, and pointed out that it might possibly have been the panel exhibited in 1867 (see below) as 'Lisière de forêt. Large ébauche. Au fond, effet de nuages très lumineux 1852. 30 x 46 cm.'.

PROV.:   Claude Earnshaw, London; Roland, Browse and Delbanco.
LIT.:   *Preview,* 43, 1958, p. 415, illus.
EXH.:   (possibly) Paris, *Etudes peintes de Th. Rousseau,* 1867 (73).
Purchased, 1958.   [*Plate 10*]

KER-XAVIER ROUSSEL
1867 – 1944

Painter of decorative subjects; born in Lorry-les-Metz; worked in Paris and L'Etang la Ville, where he died.

1034 Silenus

A Bacchanalian procession with Silenus astride an ass supported by two figures, one playing a tambour.

Millboard 9¼ x 18½ *ins.,* 23.5 x 47 *cms.*

Signed, lower right: *K. X. Roussel*

Several other paintings by Roussel which date from the period 1905-10 use the same theme and a similar composition; a *Silène ivre* of c.1910 is illustrated by L. Cousturier (*K. X. Roussel,* 1927, f.p. 56) and a *Silène* of 1905 by L. Worth (*K. X. Roussel,* 1930, pl. 9).

PROV.:   Paris, Galerie Rousso, 1951; Leicester Galleries, 1952, bought Milner-White.
EXH.:   London, Leicester Galleries, January, 1952 (50).
Presented by the Very Rev. E. Milner-White, 1963.

JAMES JEBUSA SHANNON
1862 – 1923

Portrait painter; born in Auburn, New York; worked and died in London.

23 Miss Chloe Preston.

A red-haired young woman seated, three-quarter length, facing right.

Canvas 50 x 40 *ins.,* 127 x 101.6 *cms.*

Signed, lower right: *J. J. Shannon*

Painted in 1909. The sitter was the daughter of H. E. Preston of Middle-thorpe Manor, York; she was living in the south of France in 1949 when she expressed the wish that her portrait should come to York (letter from Mrs. J. Rennie in Gallery files dated 21st May, 1949).

PROV.: Mrs. Henry Preston (the sitter's mother); Mrs. J. Rennie (the sitter's aunt).

EXH.: R.A., 1909 (459).

Presented by Mrs. J. Rennie on behalf of the sitter, 1949.

WILLIAM SHAYER
1788 – 1879

Landscape and genre painter; born in Southampton; worked in Hampshire.

126 Milking Time

A bare-footed milkmaid leans against a cow standing by a hedge with a gnarled dead tree; other cattle in the field.

Panel 24 x 19½ *ins.*, 61 x 49.6 *cms.*

Signed, lower left: *Wm Shayer*

Painted c.1850.

PROV.: I. Whitehead, York; Burton.

LIT.: *York Catalogue*, 1907, no. 39, illus. p. 26 (in reverse); *Preview*, 90, 1970, p. 821, illus.

EXH.: York, 1856 (53), lent Whitehead.

Burton Bequest, 1882.

WALTER RICHARD SICKERT
1860 – 1942

Painter of urban life; born in Munich; worked in London, Paris, Dieppe, Brighton and Bath; died at Bathampton, Somerset.

8 Old Heffel of Rowton House

Whole-length figure of a seated old man, bald and bearded, facing right, playing a violin; the canvas is faintly squared.

Canvas 22 x 16 *ins.*, 55.8 x 40.7 *cms.*

Signed, lower left: *R^d. St A.R.A.*

Painted c.1916. The signature was added later, since Sickert was not made an A.R.A. until 1924 (see Baron, p. 165). Sickert used this model, a London beggar-violinist, for several pictures; Wendy Baron lists four more oils (cat. 359, versions 1-4), one of which is inscribed *Paganini of Soho,* and a squared-up drawing in pen, chalk and ink. All these comparative examples are in private collections. Sickert also made two etchings of the subject, a large plate (12 x 10 ins.) and a small (5¾ x 4⅜ ins., illus. O. Sitwell ed., *A Free House*, 1947, f.p. 186), both almost identical to the York picture.

PROV.: Mrs. D. M. Fulford, bequeathed to the N.A.C.F., 1945.

LIT.: J. Russell, *From Sickert to 1948*, 1948, p. 18, pl. 19; *Preview*, 21, 1953, illus. cover; L. Browse, *Sickert*, 1960, p. 110; W. Baron, *Sickert*, 1973, pp. 155, 368 (cat. 359), fig. 251.

EXH.: London, Saville Gallery, 1928 (24), lent Fulford; Cairo, British Council, *International exhibition*, 1947 (31); Dijon, 1957 (35); Hull, University, *Sickert in the North*, 1968 (17).

Presented by the National Art-Collections Fund, 1945. [*Plate 31*]

591 The Butcher's Shop

A view across a street to three carcases of beef hanging outside a shop; painted in dull greys and browns.

Panel 9 x 14½ *ins., 22.9 x 36.9 cms.*

Signed, lower left: *Sickert*

Painted c.1884, very much in the Whistler manner. Wendy Baron points out a close comparison with Whistler's *Chelsea Shops* (Washington, Freer Gallery of Art, illus. D. Sutton, *Whistler*, 1966, pl. 103), and states that 'it was painted in one sitting from nature'. No.591 has been called *The Butcher's Shop, Dieppe*, but there seems to be no proof of the location.

PROV.: Mrs. Florence Holland (née Patch, a close friend of the artist at Dieppe); Redfern Gallery, 1951, bought Milner-White.

LIT.: L. Browse, *Sickert*, London, 1960, p. 110; W. Baron, *Sickert*, 1973, pp. 17, 299, 301 (cat. 21), fig. 12.

EXH.: London, Redfern Gallery, June-July, 1939 (8), November, 1939 (1), Summer, 1950 (49), Summer, 1951 (135); Sheffield, Graves Art Gallery, *Sickert*, 1957 (86), and *Conder*, 1967 (36); London and Edinburgh, Fine Art Society, *Sickert*, 1973 (3).

Presented by the Very Rev. E. Milner-White, 1951. [*Plate 21*]

924 The Visitor

Interior with a standing woman wearing a coat and hat and carrying an umbrella, taking off her gloves.

Canvas on board 14¾ x 9¾ *ins., 37.5 x 24.8 cms.*

Painted c.1908. There is another painting by Sickert entitled *The Visitor* (Baron cat. 206) which bears no resemblance to no.924; nor does a drawing of that title by Sickert in the Huddersfield Art Gallery.

PROV.: Saville Gallery; Redfern Gallery; Roland, Browse and Delbanco, 1954, bought Milner-White.

LIT.: *Preview*, 43, 1958, p. 418, illus.; L. Browse, *Sickert*, 1960, p. 110; M. Lilly, *Sickert*, 1972, pp. 60-61, pl. 17.

EXH.: London, Saville Gallery, 1928 (23), as *The Little Visitor*; Redfern Gallery, Summer, 1935 (5), as *Afternoon Visit*; Roland, Browse and Delbanco, Christmas, 1954 (22), and May-June, 1966 (30).

Presented by the Very Rev. E. Milner-White, 1958. [*Plate 32*]

1029 The Piazzetta, Venice

The Grand Canal running across the foreground with gondolas; the Piazzetta with the two standing columns, centre; the Campanile, left, and the edge of the Doge's Palace, right.

Canvas 20½ x 13¼ *ins., 33.5 x 52.1 cms.*

Signed, lower right: *Sickert*

Painted c.1901, a version of *Le Palais des Doges au crépuscule* (23½ x 18 ins., Baron cat. 138) of c.1901, now in a private collection. A closely related pastel and watercolour (21¾ x 14⅞ ins.) is in the Tate Gallery (3810). Sickert visited Venice on three occasions, the winters of 1895, 1900-01 and 1903-04. The old Campanile, which appears in the left background of no. 1029, collapsed on 14th July, 1902; an exact copy was opened in 1912.

PROV.: (possibly) J-E. Blanche; Galerie Lorenceau, Paris; Tooth's, 1950, bought Milner-White.

LIT.: *Preview,* 63, 1963, p. 597, illus.; Tate Gallery Catalogue, *Modern British Paintings,* vol. 2, 1964, p. 623; E. Forssman, *Venedig in der Kunst und im Kunsturteil des 19 Jahrhunderts,* Stockholm, 1971, p. 182, fig. 27; W. Baron, *Sickert,* 1973, p. 327 (under cat. 138).

EXH.: London, Tooth's, *Recent Acquisitions V,* 1950 (15); Edinburgh, Arts Council, *Sickert,* 1953 (11); London and Edinburgh, Fine Art Society, *Sickert,* 1973 (39).

Presented by the Very Rev. E. Milner-White, 1963. [*Plate 33*]

1044 La Rue de la Boucherie with the Church of St. Jacques, Dieppe

A public square with young trees just in blossom; the facade of St. Jacques runs down the left hand side of the picture, and there are houses across the farthest end of the square.

Panel 7½ x 9½ *ins., 19 x 24.2 cms.*

Signed and dated, lower left: *Sickert 1903*

There are many other versions of this subject by Sickert, all within the period 1902-05. Wendy Baron lists three versions of no. 1044 (under cat. 151), and four drawings (two of which are in the Musée de Rennes), all datable c.1902-03. Sickert also painted several times a very similar view with the trees in full blossom, datable c.1903-05 (Baron cat. 154, fig. 110). All these comparative oil paintings are in private collections.

PROV.: Miss N. Horsfall; Roland, Browse and Delbanco, 1950, bought Milner-White.

LIT.: L. Browse, *Sickert,* 1960, pp. 26, 68, 110, pl. 27; W. Baron, *Sickert,* 1973, pp. 70, 329 (cat. 151), fig. 105.

EXH.: London, Roland, Browse and Delbanco, December, 1948 (54), December, 1949 (30), March, 1950 (8); Edinburgh, Arts Council, *Sickert,* 1953 (103); London, Arts Council, *Sickert,* 1960 (57), and *Sickert,* 1964 (8); Hull, University, *Sickert in the North,* 1968 (12).

Presented by the Very Rev. E. Milner-White, 1963.

Sir Matthew SMITH
1879 – 1959

Figurative painter; born in Halifax; worked in London and France; died in London.

870 Girl in blue

Half-length figure of a dark-haired girl in a blue dress, holding a rose in her right hand.

Canvas 27½ x 23¾ ins., 69.9 x 60.3 cms.

Signed, lower right; *MS*

Painted c.1930; the same model appears in Smith's *Lady in Rose*, dated 1936 but possibly earlier, (exhibited, Arts Council, *Smith, paintings from the artist's studio,* 1972, no.30).

Prov.: The artist; Roland, Browse and Delbanco.

Lit.: *Preview,* 35, 1956, p. 351, illus.

Exh.: London, Roland, Browse and Delbanco, April, 1956 (7); Dijon, 1957 (40); Welsh Arts Council, *Matthew Smith,* 1966 (22).

Purchased, 1956.

Sir Stanley SPENCER
1891 – 1959

Figurative, visionary painter; born in Cookham, Berkshire; worked in London and the home counties; died in Cookham.

1031 The Deposition and Rolling Away of the Stone

The picture is divided horizontally into two parts; above, Christ on the cross with three men removing the nails, John supporting Mary left; a back view of a nude man bending, right. Below, four sleeping soldiers and two angels, one of whom rolls away the stone from the tomb as the other enters.

Canvas 39½ x 22½ ins., 110.3 x 57.2 cms.

Painted in 1956.

Prov.: Tooth's, 1956, bought Milner-White.

Lit.: *Preview,* 63, 1963, p. 601, illus.

Exh.: London, Tooth's, February, 1956 (11).

Presented by the Very Rev. E. Milner-White, 1963.   [*Plate 45*]

George Clarkson STANFIELD
1828 – 1878

Marine and landscape painter; son of Clarkson Stanfield (1793-1867, see vol. 2, pp. 79-80); born in London; worked in London and travelled widely in Europe; died in Hampstead.

295 Swiss Landscape

By a rough wooden chalet, in the left foreground, a woman holding a spindle talks to another holding a wooden milk churn; to the right a stream with a rustic bridge and a path leading to other chalets among trees; snow-covered peaks in the distance.

Canvas 24 x 36 *ins.*, 61 x 91.4 *cms.*

Lit.: *York Catalogue*, 1907, no. 18.

Burton Bequest, 1882.

Henry STANIER
active 1847 died 1892

History painter; born in Birmingham; worked in Birmingham; travelled in Paris, Algiers, Spain and Greece.

158 Benvenuto Cellini

Cellini, in red hose and a brown jerkin wearing a sword and a feathered cap, sits at a table contemplating a marble statuette, left; in the foreground lie the capital of a column, marble heads and a standing figurine; Cellini (1500-71) the Florentine sculptor and silversmith whose dramatic *Autobiography* made him a popular historical figure.

Panel 7⅞ x 6½ *ins.*, 20 x 16.5 *cms.*

Signed and dated, lower right: *H. Stanier 1855*, and inscribed in French, verso, with title, artist and date, and *D'après Fauvelet*.

The inscription might indicate that the picture is copied from a painting or print by J-B Fauvelet (1819-83), the French genre and history painter.

Lit.: *York Catalogue*, 1907, no. 86.

Burton Bequest, 1882.

ascribed to Sidney STARR
1857 – 1925

Painter of urban life; born in Hull; worked in London, emigrated to America in 1892; died in New York.

922 Fete Day

A sportsground with flags and sacking fence; banner at either side of entrance reads 'Upper Wel . . .'

Panel 5½ x 9¾ *ins.*, 14 x 24.7 *cms.*

Prov.: Roland, Browse and Delbanco, 1952, bought Milner-White.

Lit.: *Preview*, 43, 1958, p. 415.

Exh.: London, Roland, Browse and Delbanco, *Christmas Exhibition*, 1952 (39).

Presented by the Very Rev. E. Milner-White, 1958.

Philip Wilson STEER
1860 – 1942

Painter of landscape and domestic genre; born at Birkenhead; worked in Gloucester, Paris and London, where he died.

919 Boats on the beach, Southwold

Two rowing boats on the beach, centre, with figure seated between them; a sailing boat, left, with two seated fishermen; another sailing boat, right.

Panel 8 x 10¾ ins., 20.3 x 27.3 cms.

Signed, lower left: *P.W.S.*

Painted c.1888-89. Three other small panels of coast scenes by Steer are also datable to this period: *Bathing Machines* (8 x 9½ ins.), formerly with Lockett Thomson; *Two Girls on Walberswick Beach* (10 x 14 ins.), in Plymouth Art Gallery and *Boulogne Sands—children digging* (8 x 10½ ins.), in the collection of Martin Halperin (Laughton cat. 41, 43, 44, respectively).

PROV.: Steer studio sale, Christie's, 16-17th July, 1942 (188), bought Brockbank; Leger Gallery; R. L. H. Lancaster, 1943; Dr. Mary Woodall, 1943; Roland, Browse and Delbanco, 1947; bought Milner-White, 1958.

LIT.: D. S. McColl, *Philip Wilson Steer*, 1945, p. 196; *Preview*, 43, 1958, pp. 413-15, illus. cover; B. Laughton, *Philip Wilson Steer*, Oxford, 1971, p. 129 (cat. 42).

EXH.: London, Roland, Browse and Delbanco, May-June, 1947 (24).

Presented by the Very Rev. E. Milner-White, 1958.   [*Plate 21*]

1027 Dover Coast

A flat overcast seascape with ships, left, and low cliffs, right.

Canvas 16 x 24 ins., 40.7 x 61 cms.

Painted c.1918.

PROV.: Redfern Gallery; H. E. Bates; Roland, Browse and Delbanco, 1950, bought Milner-White.

LIT.: *Preview*, 63, 1963, p. 598, illus.; B. Laughton, *Philip Wilson Steer*, Oxford, 1971, p. 152 (cat. 542).

EXH.: London, Adams Gallery, *Steer*, 1949 (19), lent Bates; Roland, Browse and Delbanco, May, 1950 (25).

Presented by the Very Rev. E. Milner-White, 1963.

1032 Kimono

Full-length standing figure of a woman in a kimono, her hand on her chin.

Canvas 24 x 9 ins., 61 x 22.8 cms.

Also known as *Woman standing in a yellow kimono* (Steer papers, British Museum Print Room). Painted c.1894, a preliminary study for *The Japanese Gown*, painted 1894-96 (50 x 40 ins., Laughton cat. 167) in the National Gallery, Melbourne. Another study (27 x 18 ins., Laughton cat. 162) is in a private collection. The model for no.1032 was Rose Pettigrew; her features, and the pose, were altered for the Melbourne picture.

PROV.: Dermod O'Brien; Dr. Brendan O'Brien; January, 1946, bought Leicester Galleries; sold Christie's, 26th June, 1953 (164), bought Roland, Browse and Delbanco; bought Milner-White.

LIT.: D. S. McColl, *Philip Wilson Steer*, 1945, p. 195; *Preview*, 63, 1963, p. 599, illus.; B. Laughton, *Philip Wilson Steer*, Oxford, 1971, pp. 62-63, 136 (cat. 161).

EXH.: London, Leicester Galleries, Winter, 1946 (75), as *Kimona.*

Presented by the Very Rev. E. Milner-White, 1963.   [*Plate 23*]

FRANK STONE
1800 – 1859

Narrative painter; born Manchester; worked and died in London.

313 Mated

On a balcony a seated young woman looks down on a young man who kneels before her and holds her hand; 17th-century costumes.

Canvas 34½ x 44 *ins.*, 87.6 x 11.8 *cms.*

One of a pair of pictures exhibited by Stone at the R.A. in 1847; its pendant, *The Impending Mate,* shows the same two figures engaged in a game of chess. Both paintings were engraved by W. H. Simmons and published by Gambart in 1849.

PROV.: W. M. Nurse sale, Fosters, London, 30th June, 1848 (with *The Impending Mate*); John Whittaker of Ashton under Lyme sale, Christie's, 6th May, 1865 (20 and 21; with *The Impending Mate*), bought Wilkinson; Moore, McQueen & Co., Christie's, 27th April, 1866 (209), bought Burton.

LIT.: *The Art Journal,* 1849, p. 100, and 1856, p. 335 illus. (engraving); J. L. Roget, *History of the Old Watercolour Society,* 1891, vol. 2, p. 219; *York Catalogue,* 1907, no. 38, illus. frontispiece.

EXH.: R.A., 1847 (422).

Burton Bequest, 1882.

MARCUS STONE
1840 – 1921

Narrative painter; son of Frank (q.v.); born, worked and died in London.

203 The Convict

A young man sitting dejectedly in a cell, while a warder brings in an old woman to visit him, right.

Canvas 30 x 25 *ins.*, 76.2 x 63.5 *cms.*

Signed and dated, lower left: *MS* (in monogram) *1858-60*

LIT.: *York Catalogue,* 1907, no. 113.

Burton Bequest, 1882.

ARTHUR STUDD
1863 – 1919

Painter of landscape and urban life; born at Hallerton Hall, Leicestershire; worked in London, Paris and Brittany; travelled to Tahiti and Samoa; died in London.

918   Venetian Twilight

A gondola at mooring posts with the church of Santa Maria della Salute in the background.

Panel 5 x 8½ ins., 12.7 x 21.6 cms.

This picture would seem to relate to the eight paintings entitled 'A Venetian Lyric', lettered A-H, which were included in the Alpine Club exhibition of 1911, one of which is now in the Tate Gallery (3275). The loose, sketchy, quality of the brushwork, through which a figure in long flowing drapery drawn in pencil is visible at the right side, suggests that no. 918 was a study rather than a finished work.

PROV.:   Roland, Browse and Delbanco, bought Milner-White.
Presented by the Very Rev. E. Milner-White, 1958.

921   Washing Day

A flight of wooden steps leading up to a house with laden washing lines hanging either side.

Panel 8½ x 6¼ ins., 21.6 x 15.9 cms.

The bright colours and thick impasto technique suggest a date before 1894, when Studd was first influenced by Whistler.

PROV.:   Roland, Browse and Delbanco, 1955, bought Milner-White.
EXH.:   London, Roland, Browse and Delbanco, *Christmas Exhibition*, 1955 (32).
Presented by the Very Rev. E. Milner-White, 1958.

JOHANN TILL
1827 – 1894

History painter; born and worked in Vienna; travelled in Italy and France; died in Vienna.

376   Pan.

Pan sitting by a stream playing his pipes, with ducks in the foreground.

Canvas 47 x 23½ ins., 119.4 x 59 cms.

Signed, lower right: *Till J.*

LIT.:   *York Catalogue*, 1907, no. 99.
Burton Bequest, 1882.

HENRY TONKS
1862 – 1937

Figurative painter; born in Solihull; worked and died in London.

1026　The Toilet

Interior with two young girls seated face to face; one in profile to right, wearing a flowered white gown, one wearing a white chemise holding a flower, looking half left.

Canvas 26½ x 36½ ins., 67.3 x 92.7 cms.

Painted in 1896.

PROV.: The artist; Sir Augustus Daniel; Leicester Galleries, 1951, bought Milner-White.

LIT.: J. Hone, *Life of Henry Tonks*, 1939, pp. 52, 53, 80, 82, 355; *Preview*, 63, 1963, p. 600, illus.

EXH.: N.E.A.C., 1896 (42); London, National Gallery, *British Painting*, 1940 (544), lent Sir A. Daniel; Leicester Galleries, *Collection of the late Sir Augustus Daniel*, 1951 (52).

Presented by the Very Rev. E. Milner-White, 1963. [*Plate 26*]

WILLIAM TOWNSEND
1909 – 1973

Figurative painter; born in Wandsworth, London; worked in London; died in Banff, Alberta, Canada.

705　St. Helen's Square, York

View across the square towards St. Helen's church on a snowy, winter day.

Canvas 30 x 24 ins., 76.2 x 61 cms.

Painted in 1954, the second of two canvases painted from drawings made in York in January 1954. The first version (24 x 20 ins.) was in the artist's possession.

EXH.: Manchester, Arts Council, *British Painters of Today*, 1957 (29).

Purchased as the Evelyn Award, 1954.

HENRY SCOTT TUKE
1858 – 1929

Portrait and figure painter; born in York; worked in London, Paris and Cornwall; died at Swanpool, near Falmouth.

268　The Misses Santley

Three half-length figures singing together; from the left, Carrie Yates in profile facing right; Gertrude Santley by her side looking right, and Edith Santley, full face, holding the music book before her.

Canvas 26 x 38½ *ins.*, *66 x 97.8 cms.*

Signed and dated, lower right: *H. S. Tuke 1880*

The portrait was painted when the three girls were students at the Slade School of Art in London as a present from Mrs. Santley to her husband, Charles Santley, a famous tenor.

PROV.: Charles Santley; his daughter, Gertrude Meiggs (née Santley).

LIT.: *The Magazine of Art*, 1879-80, p. 351; M. T. Sainsbury, *Henry Scott Tuke*, 1933, pp. 33-44, illus. f.p. 44.

EXH.: R.A., 1880 (163).

Presented by Mrs. Gertrude Meiggs, 1935.

FRED UHLMAN
1901 –

Figurative painter; born Stuttgart; has worked in Paris and London.

570 Street corner in St-Servan

Moonlit Breton street scene; a road junction with a cafe extreme left, and the 'Hôtel de Servans' extreme right; St-Servan is by St-Malo in Brittany.

Canvas 18 x 24 *ins.*, *45.7 x 61 cms.*

Signed and dated, lower right: *Uhlman/49*

EXH.: London, Leicester Galleries, *McCall, Uhlman and Bone*, 1950 (15).

Presented by the artist, 1950.

WOUTER VERSCHUUR
1812 – 1874

Born and worked in Amsterdam; died in Vorden.

5 Horses with a Groom

Two horses held by a groom at the gateway of a castle.

Panel 8 x 11 *ins.*, *20.3 x 27.9 cms.*

Signed and dated, bottom left: *W Verschuur ft 1846*

LIT.: *York Catalogue*, 1907, no. 27.

Burton Bequest, 1882.

DAME ETHEL WALKER
1861 – 1951

Figurative painter; born in Edinburgh; worked in London and Yorkshire; travelled in France and Spain; died in London.

42 Robin Hood's Bay in winter

Robin Hood's Bay, on the Yorkshire coast, south of Whitby; trees in the left foreground; houses on a cliff top, middle distance right, with a headland beyond; the wide bay to the left and centre.

Canvas 25 x 30 *ins., 63.5 x 77.2 cms.*

Painted in or before 1947.

PROV.: Agnew, 1947, bought Milner-White.

LIT.: *Preview*, 5, 1949, p. 50, illus.

EXH.: London, Agnew's, November-December, 1947 (52); Scarborough, *Yorkshire Artists*, 1949 (90); London, Tate Gallery, *Ethel Walker*, 1952 (21); Nottingham, *Women Artists*, 1953 (122); Dijon, 1957 (36).

Presented by the Very Rev. E. Milner-White through the York Civic Trust, 1949.

43 Prize Bouquet with Grapes

A small dish with a bunch of purple grapes and a bowl of fruit and flowers.

Canvas 16 x 20 *ins., 40.6 x 50.8 cms.*

Painted in 1936.

PROV.: Barbizon House; Renaissance Galleries, 1936, Wertheim Gallery; Leicester Galleries, 1946, bought Sir Edward Marsh, presented to the C.A.S.

EXH.: London, Barbizon House, *Ethel Walker*, 1936 (10); Renaissance Galleries, November, 1936 (8); Wertheim Gallery, December, 1936 (10); Leicester Galleries, November, 1946 (122), as *Still Life, Fruit;* Scarborough, *Yorkshire Artists*, 1949 (83).

Presented by the Contemporary Art Society, 1948.

650 Decoration: Morning

A standing female nude balancing a pitcher on her head, on a cliff top; with three other female figures.

Canvas $74\frac{1}{2}$ x 50 *ins., 189.2 x 127 cms.*

Painted c.1936.

Related stylistically and iconographically to a number of large decorative pieces with symbolic or idyllic themes which date from c.1910 onwards. A signed and dated pencil study (16 x 13 ins.) for the companion piece, *Decoration: Evening,* shown at the N.E.A.C. in 1936, no.102, is also in the Gallery's collection.

PROV.: The artist; the artist's executor, H. A. Upton.

LIT.: *Preview*, 20, 1952, pp. 222, 224, illus. cover.

EXH.: N.E.A.C., 1936 (87).

Presented by H. A. Upton, 1952.

894 Landscape at Robin Hood's Bay

A hilly wooded landscape with cattle on a sunny day; a distant glimpse of the sea, far left.

Canvas 25 x 60 *ins., 63.5 x 152.4 cms.*

Probably painted c.1945.

Presented anonymously, 1957.

Edward Matthew WARD
1816 – 1879

History and narrative painter; born and worked in London; travelled in Germany; died in London.

349 Hogarth's Studio in 1739

A group of foundling children admiring Hogarth's portrait of Captain Coram framed on an easel, while Hogarth and Coram hide behind it, on the right.

Canvas 47½ x 65 *ins.*, 120.6 x 165.1 *cms.*

Signed and dated, lower left: *E M Ward/RA/1863*

When the picture was exhibited in Birmingham in 1864 the following quotation appeared in the catalogue: 'Holiday visit of foundlings to view the portrait of Captain Coram. Hogarth painted a splendid portrait of Thomas Coram, the grand old sea-captain, who spent his fortune in cherishing deserted children, and in his old age was not ashamed to confess that he had spent his life in doing good . . We hope they still teach every little boy and girl foundling to murmur a prayer for Thomas Coram—Sala's Life of Hogarth'. The reference was to Sala's essays on Hogarth which had appeared in *The Cornhill Magazine* in 1860, to be issued in book form in 1866.

Thomas Coram (c.1668-1751), supported by influential citizens, obtained a Royal Charter for the Incorporation of the Foundling Hospital in London on 20th November, 1739. It was completed in 1745 and many of the furnishings still survive in a new building on the old site at 40 Brunswick Square. William Hogarth (1697-1764) presented his portrait of Coram to the Hospital on 14th May, 1740, and the frame on 1st April, 1741 (see B. Nicholson, *The Treasures of the Foundling Hospital*, Oxford, 1972, pp. 1-10 and 68).

Ward's picture presents an optimistic view of Coram's philanthropy and reflects Hogarth's great popularity in the 19th century. The picture was painted for Duncan Dunbar, according to an old label, verso.   A preliminary version was with F. W. Cosens of Queen's Gate, London, in 1872.

Prov.: Duncan Dunbar sale, 30th April, 1864 (bought in), and 19th May, 1866 (43), bought Burton.

Lit.:   *The Art Journal*, 1863, pp. 97, 103; *The Magazine of Art*, 1878, p. 18; J. Dafforne, *The Life and Works of Edward Matthew Ward*, 1879, pp. 48-50; *York Catalogue*, 1907, no. 17, illus. p. 13; *Preview*, 90, 1970, p. 819, illus.

Exh.:   R.A., 1863 (199); Birmingham, Society of Artists, 1864 (52); York, 1879 (167).
Burton Bequest, 1882.   [*Plate 9*]

George Frederick WATTS
1817 – 1904

Figurative painter; born in London; worked in London; travelled in Italy; died at Limnerslease, Compton, near Guildford (in a house which is now the Watts Gallery).

1 Progress

A horseman with a bow symbolic of progress appearing in the sky above four seated figures symbolic of antiquarianism, materialism, sloth and optimism (see below).

Canvas 42 x 22 *ins.*, 106.8 x 55.9 *cms.*

Begun in 1888 but not considered complete until 1904 (Mrs. Watts' *Notebooks* in the Watts Gallery, p. 121). Another larger version (canvas 111 x 56½ ins.) begun in 1902 and left incomplete at the artist's death, is now in the Watts Gallery.

The idea for the composition first came to Watts when staying at Harrogate in July, 1888. The rider was intended 'to represent the progress of spiritual and intellectual ideals' while the four figures symbolise different reactions to progress. At the extreme left, the bald-headed figure crouched over his book illuminated by a candle, symbolises the antiquarian buried in the past; the central figure, bending towards a pile of gold, is concerned only with material wealth, while that on the extreme right shielding his eyes from the light of the horseman, represents sloth. The youthful figure beside him—the only one looking towards the rider—symbolises the awakening response to progress.

PROV.: The artist; New Gallery, 1904, bought Miss Ethel M. Colman and Miss Helen C. Colman; 1949, bequeathed by Ethel Colman to the N.A.C.F.

LIT.: H. W. Shrewsbury, *The Visions of an Artist: Studies in G. F. Watts*, 1918, pp. 79-86, illus.; R. Chapman, *The Laurel and the Thorn—a study of Watts*, 1945, p. 148; *Preview*, 68, 1964, pp. 640-41, illus.

EXH.: London, New Gallery, 1904 (45); Manchester, Edinburgh and Newcastle, *Watts*, 1905, lent by the Misses Colman; London, Whitechapel Art Gallery, *Watts*, 1974 (43).

Presented by the National Art-Collections Fund, 1949. [*Plate 25*]

2 Ararat

A blue mountain with the moon rising behind it, the scene of the Biblical Flood (*Genesis VIII*).

Canvas 34¾ x 15¾ *ins.*, 88.3 x 40 *cms.*

Signed, lower right: *G. F. Watts*

Painted c.1885. An extract from a letter dated 22nd August, 1902 from Mrs. Watts to Miss Ethel Colman reads: 'The picture of Ararat was painted some years before . . . [1887]. Ararat is of course a poetical name . . .'. Referring to a larger version of the same subject she wrote 'In the poetic representation of the heights upon which the ark rested was safe may be traced a theme which runs through all Mr. Watts symbolic pictures; one which reveals the artist's own profound belief in the Love which envelops the whole universe. The first hint of this may be discovered in the more philosophic utterance *Time and Oblivion*; it becomes more accentuated in Chaos and still more in The Court of Death and so onward until in the later years with increasing force it appears in *Love and Life*, in the *All pervading* and in *Love Triumphant*' (*Notebooks*, p. 5). This larger version (canvas 46 x 27 ins.)

was exhibited at the Grosvenor Gallery in 1885 when it was purchased by William Carver, passing from his collection to Douglas Freshfield in 1890. It differs in minor details from the York version by including distant mountains to the right and left of Ararat and it omits the rising moon.

PROV.:   The artist, September, 1902, bought Miss Ethel M. Colman and Miss Helen C. Colman; 1949, bequeathed by Ethel Colman to the N.A.C.F.

LIT.:   W. Bayes, *The Landscapes of G. F. Watts*, n.d., illus. pl. LV.

EXH.:   Australia, Melbourne, 1889; Hanley, Staffordshire, 1890; London, Alpine Club, 1894; Southwark, 1895; London, Whitechapel Art Gallery, *Watts,* 1974 (39).

Presented by the National Art-Collections Fund, 1949.   [*Plate 24*]

3   The Bay of Naples

The Bay of Naples with a snow-capped Vesuvius in the background.

Canvas 18 x 29 *ins., 45.7 x 73.7 cms.*

Signed, lower left: *G F Watts*

A larger version of the same subject (39 x 48 ins., in the Watts Gallery) was painted in 1888 at the Villa Baron in Mentone from gouache sketches made the same year at Naples. The York picture may date from the same time, though it was eventually among a number of pictures which Watts completed and signed, for Agnews, c.1896. A slight sketch for the composition (11 x 8 ins.) is also in the Watts Gallery. There are minor differences between the York picture and the Watts Gallery versions, in handling and in the range of hills on the right (which is more extensive in the York picture).

PROV.:   The artist, c.1896, bought Agnew; bought by a Scottish collector; 1906, sold through Agnews to the Misses Colman; 1949, bequeathed by Ethel Colman to the N.A.C.F.

LIT.:   *Preview,* 9, 1950, p. 101. illus., and 68, 1964, p. 640.

EXH.:   London, Alpine Club, 1894.

Presented by the National Art-Collections Fund, 1949.

4   Study for Coriolanus

On a grey-brown ground a sepia drawing of three half-length seated female figures, facing left.

Tempera on canvas 23 x 19½ *ins., 58.5 x 49.6 cms.*

A preliminary study for the *Coriolanus* painted for Lord Landsdowne at Bowood in 1860. The four parts of the full-size cartoon are now in the Watts gallery.

PROV.:   Kensington Gallery.

Purchased, 1949.

393   The Saxon Sentinels

A warrior holding a spear standing on a rock looking down at a sleeping boy crouched at his feet; a large hound stands beside the warrior, gazing right.

Canvas 96 x 60 *ins., 243.8 x 152.4 cms.*

No.393 suffered considerable damage from unscientific restoration in 1906, though there is evidence that its condition had deteriorated even before this, probably due to the instability of pigments used by Watts which is evident in other works. In particular during the 1906 restoration an area on the left of the picture showing a beacon with a lamp suspended from its cross beam was totally obliterated. The picture was last cleaned and restored in 1968 but much of the modelling has been lost in the draperies.

A label, verso, giving Watts' address in Cambridge Road, Edgware—where he lived in 1848—suggests a date of about this time for no.393, which was actually painted in Dorchester House. Watts seems to have worked on *The Saxon Sentinels* after his removal to a larger studio at 30, Charles Street, Mayfair. He exchanged the finished picture c.1850 for 'a little piano'.

No.393 is one of Watts' pictures of 'representative men' for a vast scheme called *The House of Life* (comparable in scope to that of Edvard Munch) which was intended to trace the progress of Man's development through the ages in relation to the cosmic forces of the universe. The scheme was never completed as an entity, though many of Watts' later pictures such as *Time and Oblivion* reflect the theme. Another painting directly related to the project is the large picture *Aristides and Bayard* (120 x 84 ins., Watts Gallery) datable c.1848-52 but never completely finished. In its visionary and heroic treatment of a theme from early British history, no.393 is also linked to Watts' other works on this subject—his *Caractacus led in triumph through the streets of Rome* and *Alfred inciting the Saxons to rebel against the Danes*.

PROV.: The artist, c.1850, London art market; Burton.

LIT.: A. West, 'The Cosmopolitan Club', *Cornhill Magazine*, vol. XV, 1890, pp. 167-68; *The Magazine of Art*, October, 1892, p. iv, and 1893, p. 286, illus.; *York Catalogue*, 1907, no. 19, illus. p. 14; M. S. Watts, *George Frederic Watts, The Annals of an Artist's Life*, 1912, vol. I, pp. 101, 131; N. Gillow, 'The Conservation of the Saxon Sentinels', *Preview*, 92, 1970, pp. 836-39, illus.

EXH.: York, 1866 (868), lent Burton; London, New Gallery, Winter, 1896-97 (4). Burton Bequest, 1882.

BERNARD WEISER
born 1822 active 1835 – 1861

History painter; born at Tournai; worked in Antwerp.

159 Ribera and his family

The artist seated at his easel, right, painting his wife and daughter, seated left; through the window a view across the bay of Naples to Vesuvius; José Ribera (1591-1652, called Lo Spagnoletto), born in Spain, settled in Naples c.1616; his wife and daughter were frequently identified as his models.

Panel 14 x 18 *ins.*, 35.6 x 46.9 *cms.*

Signed and dated, left: *B. Weiser 1861*

Despite the traditional title, *Ribera and his Daughters,* it would seem that Ribera is shown painting his wife and daughter.

LIT. :   *York Catalogue,* 1907, no. 92.

EXH. :   London, Crystal Palace Picture Gallery, 1864, as *Spagnoletto and his daughters.*

Burton Bequest, 1882.

HENRY BRITTAN WILLIS
1810 – 1884

Landscape painter; born in Bristol; worked in London, travelled briefly to America; died in London.

353   Harvest in Sussex: the day's work done

A haycart with a man, a woman and children in it, drawn by four oxen and guided by a boy, foreground; hills and a windmill, right, and a hayfield with oxen and a haycart, left background.

Canvas 46 x 60 *ins.,* 116.8 x 152.4 *cms.*

Signed and dated, lower left: *H B Willis/59*

LIT. :   *The Art Journal,* 1859, p. 80; *York Catalogue,* 1907, no. 52.

EXH. :   B.I., 1859 (448); Liverpool, 1859 (375).

Burton Bequest, 1882.

ALFRED WOLMARK
1877 – 1961

Painter of urban life; born in Warsaw; worked and died in London.

47   Ice Cream Man, Concarneau

A man in a blue cap, leaning on a two-wheeled ice-cream cart with a canopy.

Millboard 19 x 16 *ins.,* 48.3 x 40.6 *cms.*

Signed, lower right: *AW*

One of a number of pictures painted at Concarneau, Brittany, during Wolmark's honeymoon there in 1911.

PROV. :   Leicester Galleries, 1947, bought Milner-White.

LIT. :   *Preview,* 36, 1956, pp. 359-62, illus.

EXH. :   London, Leicester Galleries, *Alfred Wolmark,* 1947 (30); Dijon, 1957 (39); Arts Council, *Decade 1910-20,* 1965 (89).

Presented by the Very Rev. E. Milner-White, 1948.

ALFRED JOSEPH WOOLMER
1805 – 1892

Painter of domestic genre; born in Exeter; worked in Italy and London; died in London.

168 The Evening Hymn

A girl seated at the piano playing a piece entitled 'Evening Hymn'; a young man stands behind her at a window.

Canvas 14 x 12 *ins., 35.6 x 30.5 cms.*

Signed, verso: *A J Woolmer.*

According to a nineteenth-century MS. list of Burton's collection (Gallery archive), no. 168 was also known as *The Music Lesson.*

LIT.:   *York Catalogue,* 1907, no. 107.
EXH.:   Birmingham, Society of Artists, 1859 (206); (possibly) B.I., 1864 (146), as *The Music Lesson.*
Burton Bequest, 1882.

BRYAN WYNTER
1915 –

Abstract artist; born in London; has worked in London and St. Ives.

1003 Under Mars

Abstract linear composition in black, white and red on pale blue.

Canvas 84 x 36 *ins., 213.4 x 91.4 cms.*

Painted c.1959.

PROV.:   Waddington Galleries, bought by the C.A.S.
EXH.:   Kassel, *Dokumenta II,* 1959 (11); London, Waddington Galleries, *Bryan Wynter,* 1959 (26).
Presented by the Contemporary Art Society, 1962.

JACK BUTLER YEATS
1871 – 1957

Figurative, visionary painter; born in London, brother of the poet W. B. Yeats; worked in London, Sligo and Dublin; died in Dublin.

915 'That we may never meet again'

Two insubstantial figures; a man in a hat, left, with his back to the spectator, looking towards a bearded man, right.

Canvas 18 x 24 *ins., 45.7 x 60.9 cms.*

Signed, lower right: *Jack B Yeats*

Painted c.1955.

PROV.:   Waddington Galleries, 1956.
LIT.:   *Preview,* 43, 1958, pp. 416-17, illus.
EXH.:   Belfast, 1956 (40); London, Waddington Galleries, *Later Works by Jack B. Yeats,* 1958 (8); York, *Jack B. Yeats,* 1960 (49); Venice, *XXXI Biennale* (Irish Pavilion), *J. B. Yeats,* 1962; Dublin, New York, *Yeats Centenary,* 1971-72 (142).
Purchased, 1958.   [*Plate 46*]

APPENDIX

APPENDIX.

ALLORI, C. (1577-1621), after
458   Judith with the head of Holofernes
Canvas 142.2 × 114.3 *cms.* Copy of the painting in the Pitti Gallery, Florence.

AMICONI, Jacopo (1682?-1752)
1152   Mrs. Elizabeth Thompson (d. 1753), née Croft, of Stillington
Canvas 76.2 × 63.5 *cms.* Inscribed on relining, verso, *Painted by Sig^r Amiconi 1737.* Considerably restored.
Presented by Mrs. V. I. C. Knox, 1968.

ANDERSON, T. Percival (1884-1936)
341   Arthur Perceval Purey-Cust (1828-1916), Dean of York
Canvas 120 × 95.3 *cms.,* signed and dated 1907.
Presented by Mrs. E. M. Lloyd, 1917.

357   Mrs. Edith Anderson (1874-1945), née Baker, of York
Canvas 115 × 87 *cms.,* signed and dated 1907.
Presented by R. W. Anderson, 1946.

ARMFIELD, George (active 1840-67)
156   The Bone of Contention
Canvas 22.9 × 30.5 *cms.,* signed and dated 18(72?).
Bequeathed by Mrs. Hannah Deighton, 1913.

319   Stag and Dogs
Canvas 76.7 × 121.9 *cms.,* signed and dated 1858. Damaged.
Burton Bequest, 1882.

ATKINSON, Amy B. (active 1892-1900)
185   The Lamp
Canvas 40 × 32.4 *cms.*
Bequeathed by Major R. W. Richardson, 1916.

BANKS, Thomas (1826-96)
1199   Henry Baines (1793-1878), botanist of York
Canvas 76.2 × 63.5 *cms.*
Transferred from the Yorkshire Museum, 1971.

BARRETT, George (1732?-84), attributed
479   Lakeland Landscape
Canvas 155 × 236.2 *cms.* In ruinous condition.

BARTHEL, T. (active 1892)
179   An Aside in the theatre
Canvas 35.6 × 45.1 *cms.,* signed and dated 1892.
Bequeathed by Major R. W. Richardson, 1916.

BATTY, J. (active 1772-99)

1204   St. Mary's Abbey, York
Canvas 64.8 × 102.9 *cms.*, signed and dated 1773.

1205   The Manor Shore, York
Canvas 62.2 × 100.3 *cms.* Attributed to Batty.
Both transferred from the Yorkshire Museum, 1971.

BEAUMONT, Anne (active 1820-54)

568   The Groves Quartet
Canvas 86.4 × 111.8 *cms.*, signed and dated 1854.
A York group: Mr. Hunt (violin), John Groves (viola), Benjamin Shaw (cello, to whom the painting is inscribed) and Dr. Simpson (flute).
Presented by Mrs. King and Miss Groves of Harrogate, 1951.

BEAVIS, Richard (1824-96)

244   Marauders swimming the Tweed with stolen cattle
Canvas 30.5 × 40.6 *cms.*, signed and dated 1872.
Burton Bequest, 1882.

BELL, John (1823-81)

484   York from Scarborough railway bridge
Canvas 63.5 × 91.5 *cms.* Exhibited York, 1866 (288).

487   York from Skeldergate Ferry
Canvas 63.5 × 91.5 *cms.* Exhibited York, 1866 (102).
Both presented by the Trustees of W. W. Hargrove, 1919.

BLACKLOCK, William James (1816-58)

937   Scene on the Wear
Canvas 104.1 × 127 *cms.*, signed.
Presented by Mrs. Lumb of Alne, 1959.

BODDINGTON, Henry John (1811-65), see WARD, Martin Theodore, no. 1247.

BONINGTON, R. P. (1801-28), after

305   The Duenna
Canvas 35.6 × 26.7 *cms.* A slightly enlarged copy of the watercolour in the Wallace Collection (P 668) called *Meditation.*
Burton Bequest, 1882.

BOUGUEREAU, A. W. (1825-1905), after

113   Cupid and Psyche
Board 36.8 × 30.5 *cms.* From an engraving by Valadon; illus. *Preview,* 5, 1949, p. 59, as Etty.
Purchased out of the Wolstenholme Bequest, 1948.

BOWER, E. (active 1629-c.1668), after

1025 Ferdinando, second Baron Fairfax (1584-1648)
Panel 71.1 × 50.8 cms. Based on the head in Bower's 1646 portrait, (see vol. 2, p. 7, pl. 6); illus. *Preview,* 62, 1963, p. 587, as Bower.
Presented by J. B. Morrell, 1963.

BROADBRIDGE, Alma (1854-1948)

172 Tea Leaves
Canvas 55.9 × 86.4 cms., signed.
Bequeathed by Major R. W. Richardson, 1916.

BROOK, Walter Harvey (1864-1943)

366 Holy Trinity Priory, York; interior
Canvas 40.5 × 61 cms., signed and dated 1894.
Presented by Major S. Brook, 1944.

1197 Holy Trinity Priory, York; The Gatehouse
Canvas 40.5 × 30.5 cms., signed and dated 1891.
Transferred from the Yorkshire Museum, 1971.

1211 Holy Trinity Priory, York; the west bay
Canvas 66 × 35.5 cms., signed and dated 1893.
Transferred from the Yorkshire Museum, 1971.

1212 Holy Trinity Priory, York; the tower
Canvas 45 × 30 cms., signed and dated 1897.
Transferred from the Yorkshire Museum, 1971.

1264 Holy Trinity Priory, York; the Gatehouse
Canvas 56 × 40.5 cms., signed and dated 1898.
Presented by Major S. Brook, 1944.

1266 Holy Trinity Priory, York; interior
Millboard 35.5 × 50.5 cms., inscribed verso.
Presented by Major S. Brook, 1944.

1267 Holy Trinity Priory, York; the tower
Millboard 35.5 × 50.5 cms., signed and dated 1887.
Presented by Major S. Brook, 1944.

BRUNDRIT, Reginald Grange (1883-1960)

677 Glasson Dock, Lancashire
Canvas on board, 24.8 × 35 cms.
Presented by W. T. Oliver, 1953.

CAFE, Thomas Watt (1856-1925)

649 The Minstrel's Daughter
Canvas 55.6 × 60.9 cms., signed.
Bequeathed by Major R. W. Richardson, 1916.

CANO, A. (1601-67), called

967   Unknown Lady as St. Elizabeth (?)
Canvas 72.4 × 50.8 cms. Originally overpainted as Saint Apollonia; attributed to Cano and as such illustrated in *Preview,* 56, 1961, pp. 536-37, and exhibited at the R.A., 1962 (90), but more probably a composite, later work.
Purchased, 1960.

CAVE, Henry (1779-1836)

379   Todd's Warehouse, Stonegate, York
Millboard 58.4 × 74.9 cms. The same rooms were painted in watercolour by Cave in 1797; they were taken over by Robert Sunter in 1837.
Purchased, 1925.

1252   The Windmill Inn, St. George's Fields, York
Panel 28 × 40.7 cms., signed.
Transferred from the Mansion House, 1973.

1253   Cottage in Walmgate, York
Panel 13 × 16 cms. Attributed to Cave.
Presented by F. Heather, 1945.

1254   Lendal Water Tower, York, by night
Panel 13.1 × 16.5 cms.
Presented by F. Heather, 1945.

1255   Lendal Water Tower, York, evening
Panel 18.3 × 24 cms.
Presented by F. Heather, 1945.

1256   Walmgate Bar, York
Canvas 20.7 × 28 cms. Attributed to Cave.
Transferred from the Mansion House, 1973.

CHAMBERS, Thomas (1828-1910)

155   Fisherboy
Canvas 35.6 × 45.8 cms., signed and dated 1859.

187   Fisherman at home
Canvas 35.6 × 46.4 cms., signed and dated 1859.
Both Burton Bequest, 1882.

CLAXTON, Marshall (1812-81)

332   Hagar and Ishmael at the well
Canvas 147.3 × 177.8 cms., signed and dated 1842.
Presented by Dr. T. Spinks, 1889.

COLLIER, Thomas (1840-91)

297   Landscape
Canvas 60.9 × 106.7 cms.
Burton Bequest, 1882.

COLLINS, Hugh (active 1868, died 1896)
500 **Good News**
Canvas 91.4 × 71.1 *cms.*
Burton Bequest, 1882.

COOPER, John (born 1912, active 1937)
114 **The Orchestra**
Canvas 94 × 87.6 *cms.,* signed and dated 1930.
Presented by the Contemporary Art Society, 1938.

COPE, C. W. (1811-90) see TITIAN, after, no. 336.

CORIA, Benjamin (20th century)
410 **Cliffs and Sea**
Canvas 40.5 × 61 *cms.*
Presented by the Contemporary Art Society, 1927.

CRAFT, Percy R. (active 1882-1903)
328 **An English Garden**
Canvas 71.1 × 90.8 *cms.,* signed.
Presented by H. B. Craft, 1943.

CRAIG, H. (active 1854)
181 **Bedtime**
Panel 22.2 × 16.5 *cms.,* signed and dated 1854.
Burton Bequest, 1882.

CRAWSHAW, Lionel Townsend (1865-1949)
398 **Dancing on the Pier at Whitby**
Canvas 88.9 × 127 *cms.,* signed.
Presented by Col. H. G. Crawshaw, on behalf of the artist's widow, 1949.

DILLENS, Adolf Alexander (1821-77)
157 **Strolling Musicians**
Panel 40.6 × 53.3 *cms.,* signed and dated 1865.
Burton Bequest, 1882.

DUBUFE, Edouard-Louis (1820-83)
381 **The Magdalen by lamplight**
Copper 64.8 × 53.3 *cms.* Exhibited York, 1866 (373).
Burton Bequest, 1882.

DUDLEY, Tom (1857-after 1925)

400   St. William's College, York
Canvas 30.8 × 23.5 *cms.,* signed and dated 1881.
Presented by Mrs. Doughty of Liverpool, 1951.

DYCK, A. van (1599-1641), after

473   Thomas Wentworth, first Earl of Strafford (1593-1641)
Canvas 127 × 101.6 *cms.* Inscribed. A copy of the three-quarter length at
Petworth.
Purchased, 1934.

1171   The penitent Magdalene
Canvas 113 × 91.4 *cms.* A copy of Schaeffer, 1909, pl. 67, then at Schleissheim.
From the collection of Robert Witham of Cuton Hall, Essex, c. 1740.
Presented by Mrs. V. I. C. Knox, 1969.

EARLES, Chester (active 1842-63)

1202   Rev. Charles Wellbeloved (1769-1858), of York
Canvas 76.2 × 63.5 *cms.,* signed and dated 1859. Copy of a portrait by James
Lonsdale (1777-1839).
Transferred from the Yorkshire Museum, 1971.

FALL, George (1848-1925)

258   Castle Mills, York
Canvas 50.8 × 76.2 *cms.*
Presented by Mrs. Cammidge of York, 1947.

371   Thomas Monkhouse (1805-1902), of York
Canvas 122 × 91.5 *cms.*
Presented by the York Temperance Society, 1887.

402   The Market Cross with St. Crux, York
Canvas 71 × 91 *cms.,* signed.
Presented by Mrs. Cammidge of York, 1947.

1164   York Minster from the Dean's Garden
Canvas 45.7 × 33 *cms.,* signed.
Bequeathed by Miss Beatrice Ford, 1968.

1271   William Harland, Verger at York Minster 1865-95
Canvas 108 × 86 *cms.,* signed.

FOSTER, M. E. (active 1900)

1144   Stags in a hilly landscape
Canvas 61 × 91.4 *cms.,* signed and dated 1900.

GREY, Cedric

429   Scottish Landscape
Canvas 30.4 × 25.5 *cms.,* signed and dated 1880.

GOTCH, Thomas Cooper (1854-1931)

1207 John Francis Walker (1842-1907), Vice-President of the Yorkshire Philosophical Society
Canvas 76.2 × 63.5 *cms.*, signed.
Transferred from the Yorkshire Museum, 1971.

GRIMSHAW, Thomas (active 1850-61)

233 Unknown Lady with a plaid shawl
Canvas 76.2 × 63.5 *cms.*, signed and dated 1850.

234 Unknown seated Man
Canvas 76.2 × 63.5 *cms.*, signed and dated 1850.

467 The Wood Family; lady and gentleman with son and daughter
Canvas 178 × 132 *cms.*, signed and dated 1850.

GUY, Thomas (1847-1906)

367 Layerthorpe Bridge and Postern, York
Canvas 50.8 × 76.2 *cms.*
Presented by Mrs. Cammidge of York, 1947.

377 York Minster from Goodramgate (Mawe's Yard)
Canvas 76.2 × 63.5 *cms.*, initialled.

1196 Castle Mills, York
Canvas 45.8 × 61 *cms.*, signed.
Transferred from the Yorkshire Museum, 1971.

1269 Castle Mills, York
Millboard 17.7 × 25.1 *cms.*   Reduced version of no. 1196 above.
Evelyn Collection, 1934 (0.21, as *Jersey House*).

HARRISON, George (1882-1936)

404 The Lock, Stamford Bridge, near York
Canvas 71 × 91 *cms.*, signed and dated 1922.
Purchased, 1929.

HAUGHTON, Benjamin (1865-1924)

184 Late Afternoon
Panel 49.8 × 35.6 *cms.*

425 The Mill, Tipton St. John's, Devon
Panel 15.6 × 15.6 *cms.*
Both presented by the artist's widow, 1937.

HENSHAW, Frederick Henry (1807-91)

118 Temple of Vesta, Tivoli
Canvas 30.5 × 43 *cms.*
Bequeathed by Mrs. Hannah Deighton, 1913.

HERRING, J. F. (1795-1865), after

1014   Deacon, the London to York Carrier, on the road in winter
Canvas 45.8 × 61 cms., inscribed with signature and date 1844. An inferior version of the painting bought in at Christie's, 6 April 1973 (17), and resold at Christie's, 26 April 1974 (178).
Presented by Col. N. Innes Ware, 1962.

HIGGINS, W. (active 1808)

214   Benjamin Agar (1793-1858)
Canvas 76.2 × 63.5 cms., signed and dated 1808.

502   A middle-aged lady of the Agar family
Canvas 76.2 × 63.5 cms.
Both presented by J. Agar, 1933.

HIRST, A. (active 1886)

580   The Plumber's Arms, Skeldergate, York
Canvas 20.3 × 27.9 cms., signed and dated 1886.
Presented by T. M. Oxtoby, 1951.

HORNIBROOK, G. A., (active 1881-85)

480   York in 1644; an outpost of Sir Thomas Fairfax
Canvas 76.5 × 127 cms., signed and dated 1881.
Purchased, 1933.

HOWELL, Sam (active 1829-54)

1206   Jonah Wass (d. 1837), M.D. of York
Canvas 91.4 × 63.5 cms., signed.
Transferred from the Yorkshire Museum, 1971.

HUDSON, B. (mid-19th century)

485   A lady of the Agar family
Canvas 76.2 × 63.5 cms., signed.
Presented by J. Agar, 1933.

HUGO, V. P. (mid-19th century)

304   Head of an Arab
Canvas 21.8 × 17.2 cms., signed.

HULME, Frederick William (1816-84)

597   Rocky landscape with stream and bridge
Canvas 70.1 × 90.8 cms., signed with initials.
Burton Bequest, 1882.

IHLEE, Rudolph (active 1910-64)
 61   **El Palo: a Spanish scene**
       Canvas 50.8 × 61 cms.
       Presented by the Contemporary Art Society, 1929.

INNOCENTI, J. (19th century)
 188 **Hide and Seek**
       Panel 33.7 × 26.7 cms., signed and lated *Roma 1873.*
       Burton Bequest, 1882.

KESSEL, Jan Thomas van (1677-c.1741)
 468 **Marriage Feast**
       Canvas 71.1 × 99.1 cms., signed and dated 1709.
       Presented by R. Marsden, 1939.

KNOWLES, J. W. (1838-1931)
 342 **William Pumphrey (1817-1905), biologist and secretary of the Y.F.A.I.I.**
       Canvas 90.5 × 71 cms., signed and dated 1881.
       Presented by the artist, 1883.

 1226 **Konstantin Kumpiew, sacrist of St. Maurice's, York**
       Canvas 50.8 × 38 cms.
       Presented by the artist's daughter, 1972.

 1227 **Sir Joseph Barnby (1838-96), composer and musician**
       Canvas 61 × 50.8 cms., signed.
       Presented by the artist's daughter, 1972.

LEE, Frederick Richard (1798-1879)
 238 **Bothwell Castle, Lanarkshire**
       Millboard 22.2 × 30.5 cms.
       Burton Bequest, 1882.

LINGELBACH, J. (1622-74), manner of
 266 **Italian port scene**
       Canvas 80 × 67.3 cms.

LOWE, Arthur (1866-1940)
 488 **Clifton Grove, Clifton Hall, Nottingham**
       Panel 62.2 × 82 cms., signed.
       Presented by Mrs. A. Lowe, 1944.

LUCAS, John Templeton (1836-80)
 130 **Not Sold Yet**
       Canvas 44.5 × 60.3 cms.
       Burton Bequest, 1882.

141   The Letter Writer
Canvas 30.5 × 25.4 *cms.,* signed and dated 1877.

149   The Old Tramp
Canvas 30.5 × 25.4 *cms.,* signed and dated 1878.

LYCETT, J. (active 1811)
1257   Old Ouse Bridge, York
Panel 17.8 × 23 *cms.,* inscribed and dated 1811.
Presented by Oliver Sheldon, 1931.

M., C. A. (active early 19th century)
1156   A youth of the Hornby family, called Sir Thomas Hornby
Canvas 25.4 × 20.3 *cms.,* signed.
Presented by Miss H. Hornby and Mrs. C. Drummond, 1968.

M., H. (active late 19th century)
1248   Holy Trinity, Goodramgate, York; interior
Canvas 36 × 26 *cms.,* signed. Previously called Henry Moore (q.v.).
Evelyn Collection, 1934 (O. 18).

M., S. (active early 19th century)
483   Old Ouse Bridge, York
Canvas 68.6 × 99.1 *cms.,* signed. Another version belongs to the Merchant
Adventurers Hall, York.
Evelyn Collection, 1934   (O. 26).

McKENZIE-SMITH, B. see SMITH

MANZONI, P. (19th century)
273   Landscape
Canvas 111.8 × 86.4 *cms.,* signed.
Burton Bequest, 1882.

MARSHALL, George (1801-27)
369   William Lodge Rocliffe (1755-1839)
Canvas 75 × 63.5 *cms.* Painted in imitation of Reynolds' portrait of William
Mason (Pembroke College, Cambridge); engraved by W. J. Ward in 1822.
Presented by Miss Rocliffe of Easingwold, 1934.

MARTINETTI, Angelo (active 1850-80)
276   The Mousetrap
Panel 50.8 × 35.5 *cms.,* signed and dated 1874.
Burton Bequest, 1882.

MASCALL, Edward (active 1650-67), after

1100 **Oliver Cromwell (1599-1658) Lord Protector of England**
Canvas 76.2 × 63.5 *cms.* Based on the Mascall portrait at Huntingdon, but reversed and without the hand.
Presented by the family of the late J. B. Morrell, 1964.

MASSER, H. (mid-19th century)

615 **York: the Ouse from Skeldergate Bridge**
Canvas 50.8 × 76.2 *cms.*, signed and dated 1868.
Evelyn Collection, 1934 (O. 31).

1263 **York: the Ouse from Scarborough railway Bridge**
Canvas 50.8 × 76.2 *cms.*, signed and dated 1869.
Evelyn Collection, 1934 (O. 30).

MAYER, A. (active 1825-46)

1203 **Philip Knapton (1762-1833), musician of York**
Canvas 91.4 × 71.1 *cms.*
Transferred from the Yorkshire Museum, 1971.

MEADOWS, Edwin L. (active 1857-67)

239 **Landscape with an old mill**
Canvas 25.4 × 35.6 *cms.*, signed.
Burton Bequest, 1882.

MEAK, J. C. (active 1849)

326 **A 17th-century Dutch interior with a seated lady**
Canvas 33 × 27 *cms.*, signed and dated 1849.
Bequeathed by Major R. W. Richardson, 1916.

MIDWOOD, E. (mid-19th century)

108 **Cottage near Missenden**
Canvas 17.8 × 25.4 *cms.*, inscribed.

MONKHOUSE, C. (active 1849)

1274 **Petergate, York, from the west**
Canvas 32.5 × 25.5 *cms.*, signed, inscribed and dated 1849, verso.
Evelyn Collection, 1934 (O. 23, as W. Monkhouse).

MOORE, William I (1790-1851), father of Albert and Henry (q.v.)

183 **George Wilkinson**
Copper 30.5 × 25.4 *cms.*, signed and dated 1851.
Presented by John Bickle, 1929.

217 **John Hay**
Copper 30.5 × 25.4 *cms.*
Presented by Scarborough Corporation, 1948.

218   Unknown Man
Copper 61 × 44.5 *cms., signed.*
Purchased, 1948.

MOREL, Charles (1861-1908)
335   Sunset in south Tyrol
Canvas 74 × 98.6 *cms., signed.*
Rawdon Bequest, 1895.

MORRISON, K. F. (20th century)
115   View through a window
Canvas 55 × 48 *cms.*
Presented by the Contemporary Art Society, 1928.

MOSTYN, Tom Edwin (1864-1930)
230   Peace
Canvas 71.1 × 91.5 *cms., signed.*
Bequeathed by J. E. Champney, 1929.

MULREADY, Augustus E. (active 1863, died 1886)
125   Newsboy
Panel 31.3 × 24.2 *cms.,* signed.   Showing a placard 'Cry and Shriek from
Dublin', presumably relating to the Phoenix Park murders of 1882. Illus.,
Preview 4, 1948.
Presented by Lord Beaverbrook, 1948.

NICHOLSON, George (1787-1878)
1249   Layerthorpe Bridge and Postern, York
Canvas 28 × 35.5 *cms.*   Attributed to Nicholson.
Transferred from the Mansion House, 1973.

1250   Layerthorpe Bridge and Postern, York
Millboard 28.3 × 36 *cms.,* signed and dated 1829.
Transferred from the Mansion House, 1973.

1251   Clifford's Tower with Castlegate Postern, York
Panel 25.2 × 36 *cms.*
Evelyn Collection, 1934 (O. 22).

NIXON, M. (active 1873)
150   Still life
Board 34.9 × 39.4 *cms.,* signed and dated 1873.
Presented by Miss Dickson, 1946.

PANNINI, G. P. (1692-1765), manner of
956   Classical ruins with figures
Canvas 119.4 × 109 *cms.*   Formerly called Servandoni.
Presented by the York B Group Hospitals Management Committee, 1960.

PAOLINI, Paolo (1603-81), after

1127 Salome with the head of John the Baptist
Canvas 123.3 × 162.6 *cms.* Inferior version of the picture sold at Christie's 26 Nov. 1965 (51) as A. Grammatica, on the Florentine art market in 1967; no. 1127 was sold at Christie's on 9 April 1965 (17) as R. Manetti. The composition is now attributed to Paolini.
Purchased, 1966.

PATTEN, George (1801-65)

1198 Rev. John Kendrick (1788-1877), antiquary of York
Canvas 113 × 86.3 *cms.,* signed and dated 1846. Engraved by T. Lupton in 1847.
Transferred from the Yorkshire Museum, 1971.

PEEL, James (active 1828-50)

146 Landscape
Canvas 25.4 × 38.1 *cms.,* signed.

PERCY, Sidney Richard (1821-86)

375 A Mill near Dorking
Canvas 91.4 × 137.2 *cms.,* signed and dated 1859.
Burton Bequest, 1882.

PETHER, A. (1756-1812), style of

599 Moonlit landscape with lake and ruined abbey
Canvas 50.8 × 61 *cms.*

PETTINGER, John Frederick (1878-after 1925)

250 Wells from the Marches
Canvas 31.8 × 39.4 *cms.*
Presented by York Art Society, 1926.

POOLE, James (c.1804-84)

292 View in the Tête Noir, Switzerland
Canvas 66.7 × 91.5 *cms.,* signed.
Bequeathed by Mrs. Hannah Deighton, 1913.

RAINE, H. Keyworth (1872-c.1932)

171 Head of a Girl
Canvas 45.8 × 35.5 *cms.,* signed and dated 1931.
Presented by the artist, 1932.

278 Head of an elderly Woman
Canvas 72 × 51 *cms.*
Presented by the artist, 1913.

361 Miss de Baugay
Canvas 91.4 × 71 *cms.,* signed and dated 1927.
Presented by the artist, 1929.

362 Self portrait (as Diogenes)
Canvas 94 × 76.2 *cms.* The artist enjoyed a vogue for his candlelit portraits painted in a darkened basement in Hanover Square.
Presented by the artist, 1920.

378 James Melrose (1829-1929), Lord Mayor of York
Canvas 68.6 × 55 *cms.* Painted in 1926.
Presented by the artist, 1926.

482 George Kirby (1845-1937), first curator of York Art Gallery
Canvas 68.6 × 55.8 *cms.* Painted in 1925.
Presented by the artist, 1926.

1200 Rev. James Raine (1830-96), Chancellor of York Minster
Panel 66 × 54.8 *cms.,* signed and dated 1906. Painted posthumously, apparently from a photograph. The sitter was the artist's father.
Transferred from the Yorkshire Museum, 1971.

RAMSAY, Lady Patricia (1886-1974)
403 In the Tropics
Millboard 58.4 × 62.9 *cms.,* signed.
Presented by the Contemporary Art Society, 1933.

RANKEN, William Bruce Ellis (1881-1941)
312 Mrs. Kelsey in Pink
Canvas 101.6 × 76.2 *cms.,* signed and dated 1919.
Presented by the artist's sister, Mrs. Thesiger, 1946.

ROSA, S. (1615-74), called
248 Christ and the disciples on the road to Emmaus
Canvas 48.3 × 37.5 *cms.,* inscribed *S. Rosa,* verso, in a 17th-18th century hand.

RUBENS, P. P. (1577-1640), after
373 Virgin and Child
Canvas 101.6 × 76.2 *cms.* Copy of Rosenberg, 1905, pl. 167.

749 Hercules and Antaeus
Panel 27.9 × 30.1 *cms.* From the Violet, Lady Melchett sale, Sotheby's, 20th July, 1932 (143); a grisaille sketch based on the Rubens drawing in the Fitzwilliam (inv. no. 2181).
Presented by F. D. Lycett Green through the N.A.C.F., 1955.

RUTSON, J. (active 1868-75)
1109 Landscape with mountains and sheep
Canvas 49.5 × 71.1 *cms.,* signed and dated 1875.
Presented by Messrs. N. S., H. P., A.V. and C. E. Cooper, 1965.

SALMON, Doria (20th Century)
112 Nude with flowers (Girl in a Glasshouse)
Canvas 76.2 × 88.9 *cms., signed and dated 1944.*
Presented by the Contemporary Art Society, 1946.

SEIGNAC, Paul (1826-1904)
· 154 The Course of true love never runs smooth
Panel 32.4 × 24.1 *cms., signed.*
Burton Bequest, 1882.

SHACKLETON, William (1872-1933)
287 Mrs. John Greg
Canvas 90.2 × 66.1 *cms., signed and dated 1923.*
Presented by the sitter, 1940.

322 Goblin Garden
Canvas 95.3 × 102.9 *cms., signed and dated 1921.*
Presented by Mrs. Mary Shackleton, 1938.

387 Calvary
Oil on paper 45.8 × 44.5 *cms., signed.*
Presented by Mrs. Mary Shackleton, 1938.

McKENZIE-SMITH, B. (20th century)
116 The Bird Cage
Canvas 50.8 × 61 *cms.*
Presented by the Contemporary Art Society, 1945.

SMITH, H. (?Herbert Luther, 1811-70)
432 Sir George Strickland (1782-1874)
Canvas 112 × 87 *cms., inscribed verso, with date 1832.*
The sitter changed his name to Cholmley in 1865. From the Howsham Hall
sale, 3 Nov. 1948 (666).
Presented by J. B. Morrell, 1948.

SMITH, T. Wells (active 1879-86)
339 Alderman Robert Fawcett
Canvas, 111.8 × 86.4 *cms., signed.* Painted in 1879.
Presented by Miss Meek of Oldham, 1933.

SOLE, G. G. dal (1654-1719), after
174 The penitent Magdalene
Canvas 96.5 × 132 *cms.*
Presented by D. Shirlaw, 1923.

SOORD, Alfred Usher (1868-1915)
148 Miss Thorpe
Canvas 67.3 × 50.2 *cms.*
Presented by the Rev. G. S. Thorpe, the sitter's brother, 1939.

283   **Isabel Douthett**
       Canvas 45.7 × 35.6 cms., signed and dated 1888.
       Presented by the Misses Douthett of Whitby, 1935.

324   **Wastdale Head**
       Canvas 124.5 × 104.1 cms., signed and dated 1897.
       Purchased, 1937.

370   **Anthony Buckle (1838-1900), etcher and poet of York**
       Canvas 91.4 × 71.1 cms., signed and dated 1892.
       Presented by the sitter's daughter, Miss D. Buckle, 1937.

430   **Mrs. Lowman**
       Canvas 45.7 × 35.6 cms., signed and dated 1888.
       Presented by the Misses Douthett of Whitby, 1935.

SPREAT, William (active 1819-89)

291   **Evening on the river Walkham**
       Canvas 68.6 × 101.6 cms., signed and dated 1880.

614   **Landscape with river and fishermen**
       Canvas 68.6 × 101.6 cms., signed and dated 1880.
       Both Rawdon Bequest, 1895.

STAPYLTON, M. J. (active early 19th century)

227   **Head of St. Peter**
       Canvas 50.8 × 52.6 cms.

STOCQUART, Ildephonse (1819-89)

245   **Cattle**
       Panel 43.2 × 33.7 cms., signed.
       Burton Bequest, 1882

STOTHARD, Thomas (1755-1834), attributed

1124   **Figure Composition (Paolo and Francesca?)**
       Canvas 34.3 × 28.3 cms.
       Purchased, 1966.

SWALLOW, J. C. (active 1855-70)

153   **Boy of the Patterson family**
       Millboard 47.6 × 38.7 cms. The son of W. T. Patterson (see below).

191   **Thomas Alexander Patterson as a child**
       Millboard 63.5 × 48.9 cms.

206   **Mrs William Taylor Patterson with her youngest daughter**
       Millboard 63.5 × 48.9 cms.

257   Four children of the Patterson family
Millboard 55.9 × 71.1 *cms.* The children of W. T. Patterson.
All presented by the Misses Douthett, 1935, on behalf of Mrs. J. A. Patterson,
daughter-in-law of Prof. W. T. Patterson.

SWANICK, Harold (1866-1929)
416   Evening in the Old Priory farmyard, Wilmington, Sussex
Canvas 50.8 × 76.2 *cms.*, signed.
Acquired from the artist's estate, 1943.

TERRY, Joseph Alfred (1872-1939)
189   Yorkshire Cliffs at sunset
Canvas 50.8 × 61 *cms.*, signed.
Presented by the artist, 1924.

372   Underhill Farm, Sleights
Canvas 71.1 × 91.4 *cms.*, signed.
Purchased, 1924.

TITIAN (1477-1576), after
336   Young Woman at her toilet
Canvas 95.2 × 78.7 *cms.* Copy by C. W. Cope (1811-90) from the Titian in the
Louvre (Tietze, 1950, fig. 17).

358   Venus and Adonis
Canvas 109.3 × 134.6 *cms.* Copy, with minor variations in the left background,
of the Titian in the Prado (Tietze, 1950, fig. 221).
Rawdon Bequest, 1895.

TOWNESEND, Mabel (active 1888-1900)
289   An Airedale called Nansen
Canvas 61 × 91.5 *cms.* Exhibited York, 1900 (454).

424   Five Chickens
Canvas 20.3 × 29.2 *cms.*
Both bequeathed by Mrs. E. A. M. Piercy, 1934.

VALENTINE, J. (active 1905)
1246   Thomas Guy (1847-1906) artist of York
Canvas 122 × 92 *cms.* Painted in 1905; illus. *Yorks. Herald*, 6 Nov., 1906.
Deposited by the sitter's grand-daughter, Mrs. M. Evans, 1963.

VILA, Senen (active 1678 died 1708), after
392   Christ and the three Maries at the Tomb
Canvas 167.6 × 185.4 *cms.* In ruinous condition.
Burton Bequest, 1882.

VINALL, Joseph William Topham (1873-1953)
> **415   Evensong, Westminster Abbey**
> *Canvas* 71.1 × 91.5 *cms.,* signed.
> Presented by the artist, 1941.

W., F. (mid-19th century)
> **1265   Off Whitby; coast scene**
> *Canvas* 61 × 46 *cms.*

WALTON, George (active 1883-88)
> **1201   William Reed (1811-92), geologist of York**
> *Canvas* 101.5 × 76.2 *cms.,* signed and dated 1887.
> Transferred from the Yorkshire Museum, 1971.

WALTON, James Trout (1828-67), brother of Joseph (q.v.)
> **60   Interior of a Highland Cottage**
> *Panel* 20.3 × 30.5 *cms.,* signed and dated 1854.
> Bequeathed by Mrs. Hannah Deighton, 1913.

> **144   Vale of the Lauterbrunnen, Switzerland**
> *Canvas* 20.3 × 30.5 *cms.*   Painted c.1856.
> Bequeathed by Mrs. Hannah Deighton, 1913.

> **145   View in Scotland**
> *Canvas* 33 × 74 *cms.*
> Bequeathed by Mrs. Hannah Deighton, 1913.

> **327   Algiers**
> *Canvas* 50.8 × 104.1 *cms.,* signed. Painted c.1862.
> Presented by R. H. R. Hawkswell, 1932.

> **334   Scene in Algiers**
> *Canvas* 91.5 × 151 *cms.,* signed and dated 1862.
> Presented by the artist's step-daughter, Miss Hands, 1933.

WALTON, Joseph (active 1855-96), brother of James Trout (q.v.)
> **143   Goatherd**
> *Canvas* 43.2 × 71.1 *cms.*
> Presented by A. W. Linfoot, 1928.

> **151   Scene on a common with two donkeys**
> *Canvas* 45.7 × 61 *cms.,* signed and dated 1866(?).
> Burton Bequest, 1882.

> **401   Old Beilby, the knife-grinder**
> *Canvas* 40.7 × 30.5 *cms.,* signed and dated 1882, and verso, 1878.
> Presented by Mrs. Dudley of Liverpool, 1950.

WARD, Martin Theodore (1800-74)

306   Head of a Terrier
Canvas 35.6 × 30.5 *cms.*
Presented by P. Crombie, 1945.

422   Head of a Terrier
Canvas 14.5 × 19.5 *cms.*

423   Head of a Terrier
Canvas 14.5 × 19,5 *cms.*

427   Head of a Dog
Canvas 35.6 × 30.5 *cms.*
Presented by P. Crombie, 1945.

WARD, Martin Theodore (1800-74), and BODDINGTON, Henry John (1811-65)
1247   Two Fox Terriers in a landscape
Canvas 63.5 × 76 *cms.,* signed.
Deposited, 1960.

WATERLOW Sir Ernest Albert (1850-1919)
320   Wolf, wolf!
Canvas 100.3 x 127 *cms.,* signed.
Presented by Lady Waterlow, 1928.

WESTCOTT, Philip (1815-78)
333   Rev. James Parsons (1799-1877), Congregationalist minister of York
Canvas 142.2 × 111.8 *cms.*
Presented by Mrs. G. Leeman, 1884.

WHITTLE, Thomas the elder (active c.1854-68)
1173   Still life with fruit by a window
Canvas 40.6 × 61 *cms.,* signed with initials.
Presented by Mrs. V. I. C. Knox, 1969.

WICKHAM, Francis (20th century)
117   Farm in Devon
Canvas 50.8 x 65 *cms.,* signed.
Presented by the artist, 1932.

WINDASS, John (1843-1938)
321   After the Storm: off Whitby
Canvas 76.2 x 142.2 *cms.* Originally (?) called *Where the Rohilla went down*
(a medical ship sunk off Whitby in the First World War).

382   John Burton (1799-1882), Gallery benefactor
Canvas 111.8 × 83.8 *cms.* Windass was one of Burton's three executors, and a substantial beneficiary from his will.
Both presented by the artist, 1921.

WOOD, H. (active mid-19th century)
37a   Frisk, a Blenheim spaniel
Board 22.2 × 21 *cms., signed and dated 1855.*

37b   A Blenheim spaniel
Board 23.4 × 23.4 *cms.*
Both presented by Mr. Wood, 1930.

WRIGHT of Derby, J. (1734-97), imitator of
213   Forging the Anchor
Canvas 48.3 x 60.9 *cms.,* inscribed *Wright of Derby;* an invented composition.
Burton Bequest, 1882.

WRIGHT, Richard (1814-84)
338   Dr. William Procter (1818-80), Secretary of the Y.F.A.I.I.
Canvas 122 × 94 *cms., signed and dated 1879.*
Presented by the artist, 1887.

WYCK, Thomas (1616-77)
466   The Wreckers; stormy coast scene with tower
Canvas 161.3× 149.8 *cms.,* signed (or inscribed).

YGLESIAS, Vincent   Phillip (1845-1911)
207   Nelson's Column, Trafalgar Square
Canvas 53.3 x 31.8 *cms.,* signed.

UNKNOWN ARTISTS—PORTRAITS

223   Rev. Joseph Agar, Wesleyan Minister   c.1820
Canvas on panel 35.5 × 28 *cms.*
Presented by J. Agar, 1933.

224   Dutchman in 17th-century dress with a highcrowned hat
Canvas 61 × 50.8 *cms.* A copy.

240   Head of an old man 19th century
Panel 30.5 × 26.7 *cms.*

282   Mrs. T. Hands   c.1870
Canvas 91.5 × 71 *cms.* See no. 360 below.
Presented by Arthur W. Hands, 1946.

286   Unknown elderly lady in black   c.1860
Canvas 76.2 × 63.5 cms.

325   Unknown lady in a green dress   c.1840
Canvas 91.4 × 71.1 cms.

331   Five children of the Pigott family   c.1740
Canvas 130.1 × 191.1 cms. Identification traditional; possibly the children of Emanuel Pigott (d. 1762), grandfather of the first Baronet Pigott of Knapton.

355   A middle-aged man of the Agar family   c.1850
Canvas 111.8 × 91.4 cms.
Presented by J. Agar, 1933.

359   An elderly man of the Agar family   c.1860
Canvas 91.4 × 61 cms.
Presented by J. Agar, 1933.

360   Thomas Hands (1798-1874), Councillor of York
Canvas 91.5 × 71 cms. See no. 282 above.
Presented by Arthur W. Hands, 1946.

364   Charles, third Earl of Carlisle (1669-1738), in Peer's robes
Canvas 91.5 × 71 cms. Inscribed. Based on the head from Aikman's 1728 portrait at Castle Howard.
Purchased, 1938.

380   Joseph Agar (1832-1920), Lord Mayor of York, as a boy
Canvas 63.5 × 50.8 cms.
Presented by J. Agar, 1933.

447   John Flaxman (1755-1826), sculptor
Canvas 61 × 50.8 cms. In a red coat to right, his right hand on his cheek; formerly called Opie.
Purchased, 1912.

457   Unknown bewigged man holding a paper   c.1700
Canvas 72.4 × 59.7 cms. Possibly French in origin.

459   A Mother with her young daughter   c.1850
Canvas 142.2 × 111.8 cms. Style of Partridge.

486   Jane Burton of Saltmarsh aged 77 in 1840
Canvas 92.7 × 71.1 cms. Inscribed.

600   Unknown man with the Order of the Garter   c.1700
Canvas 118.1 × 99.1 cms.

601   Unknown lady in a blue dress   c.1700
Canvas 121.3 × 97.9 cms. Pair to no. 600; both portraits were said to have come from the second Duke of Buckingham's house in York.
Both presented by Dr. R. Petch, 1919.

1051   Unknown lady in a green dress   c.1640
Panel 27.3 × 30.5 *cms.* Illus. *Preview,* 64, 1963, p. 607 as Greenhill; a similarity with portraits of Lucy Walter has been indicated. Copy quality.
Presented by the Friends of York Art Gallery, with the aid of the Thompson Bequest, 1963.

1106   Unknown man in a brown coat   c.1730
Canvas 76.2 × 63.5 *cms.*

1107   Unknown Divine in gown and bands   c.1730
Canvas 78.7 × 67 *cms.*

1108   Unknown man in a brown coat and light wig   c.1730
Canvas 76.2 × 63.5 *cms.,* oval

1110   Unknown seated Divine in gown and bands   c.1750
Canvas 76.2 × 62.2 *cms.*

1111   Unknown lady   c.1720
Canvas 76.2 × 63.5 *cms.*

1112   Unknown elderly man   c.1860
Canvas 76.2 × 63.5 *cms.*

1113   Unknown girl in a green dress with parrot   c.1730
Canvas 127 × 101.6 *cms.* Illus. *Preview,* 72, 1965, cover.

1114   Unknown seated lady in a satin dress with a red drape   c.1730
Canvas 127 × 101.6 *cms.* Style of Jervas.

1115   Unknown seated Divine in gown and bands   c.1720
Canvas 127 × 101.6 *cms.* Style of Dahl.

1116   Unknown little girl holding a parrot   c.1730
Canvas 127 × 101.6 *cms.*
Nos. 1106-16 presented by Messrs. N. S., H. P., A. V., and C. E. Cooper, 1965.

1130   Unknown man with a red beard aged 40 in 1563
Canvas 91. 4 x 73.7 *cms.* Inscribed.
Presented by Miss E. M. Lawson Tancred, 1967.

1146   Unknown man of the Hornby family, called Jeffery Hornby   c.1800
Canvas 76.2 x 63.5 *cms.* Italian or French artist.
Presented by Miss H. Hornby and Mrs. C. Drummond, 1968.

1148   Cleopatra dissolving the pearl, called a portrait of a Princess Orsini   c.1800
Canvas 98.4 × 73.7 *cms.* Probably by an Italian artist.
Presented by Miss H. Hornby and Mrs. C. Drummond, 1968.

1158   Ann Carr aged 81 in 1774
Canvas 76.2 × 63.5 *cms.* Inscribed. Discovered beneath a canvas by Guy, no. 377 (q.v.) in 1968.

1160 Head of an old man
Panel 24.8 × 19 *cms.* Dutch 17th-century pattern.

1208 Samuel Knapton (1752-1831) musician and instrument maker of York
Canvas 94 × 73.4 *cms.*
Transferred from the Yorkshire Museum, 1971.

1270 Head of a turbanned Man in a red gown   19th century
Panel 18.5 × 14 *cms.*

1272 Unknown elderly Man with moustache   c.1890
Canvas 57 × 40 *cms.*

1273 Unknown elderly Man with moustache   c.1890
Canvas 111.5 × 86.4 *cms.*   The same sitter as in no. 1272 above.

UNKNOWN ARTISTS—NOT PORTRAITS

13 Landscape with St. John the Baptist
Canvas 50.2 × 73.7 *cms.* Illus. *Preview,* 5, 1949, p. 47 as Gaspard Dughet.
Presented by G. W. Ward, 1949.

48 Classical ruins and figures   18th century
Canvas 64.3 × 69 *cms.*
Bequeathed by Major R. W. Richardson, 1916.

123 Landscape with figures and horse   early-19th century
Canvas 30.5 × 38.1 *cms.*
Bequeathed by Major R. W. Richardson, 1916.

138 Coast scene with French ships firing   late-18th century
Canvas 36.8 × 55.9 *cms.*
Rawdon Bequest, 1895.

152 Woman with a candle blowing out a torch   17th century
Panel 27.9 × 24.1 *cms.*
Rawdon Bequest, 1895.

163 Tavern Scene   19th century
Canvas 41.3 × 31.1 *cms.*
Acquired, 1941.

166 Sailing ships approaching harbour   c.1840
Canvas 30.5 × 61 *cms.*

175 The Expulsion of Heliodorus   late-16th century
Canvas 115.6 × 162.6 *cms.*   Extensively restored; illus., *Preview,* 73, 1966,
p. 682, as Venetian early 17th century.
Presented by D. Shirlaw, 1923.

178   Coast scene near Whitby   mid-19th century
Canvas 50.8 × 76.2 cms.

186   View of Whitby   c.1900
Canvas 54 x 37.2 cms.
Presented by the Duke of Kent, 1940.

204   York from about Blue Bridge   c.1860
Canvas 34.3 × 50.8 cms.

205   York from about Fishergate   c.1860
Canvas 34.3 × 50.8 cms.
Both presented by T. Laughton, 1950.

210   Oxen ploughing at evening
Canvas 35.6 × 48.9 cms. Formerly attributed to Brascassat; probably French, c.1850.
Bequeathed by Major R. W. Richardson, 1916.

212   Old Ouse Bridge, York   early-19th century
Canvas 50.8 × 76.2 cms.

222   Head of an old man   19th century
Panel 28 × 22 cms.
Presented by J. B. Morrell, 1948

225   The Prodigal Son kneeling amongst cattle
Canvas 59.7 × 43.2 cms. The composition was engraved, untitled, for early 19th century editions of Clarke's Family Bible; probably from a Dutch original of c.1660.

226   St. Peter   19th century
Canvas 45.7 × 35.6 cms.

228   Sick Lady
Canvas 39.4 × 31.8 cms. Dutch 17th century pattern.
Rawdon Bequest, 1895.

229   Mary at the Well
Canvas 53.3 × 39.4 cms. Possibly 19th century.
Transferred from the Yorkshire Museum, 1948.

237   Sketch for a Feast   18th century
Canvas 25.4 × 35.6 cms.
Presented by W. Monkhouse, 1889.

263   Cottage in a landscape   mid-19th century
Canvas 18.4 × 25.4 cms.

265   The Gamblers   late-16th century
Panel 71.1 × 54.6 cms. Inscribed in Flemish.

303   Rose bush with a mountainous coast scene beyond
Canvas 69.2 × 99.1 cms.
Presented by the Duke of Kent, 1940.

307 **Dead Partridges late-19th century**
Millboard 41.9 × 31.8 *cms.*
Presented by J. Myers 1893.

329 **Evening Landscape c.1840**
Canvas 24.7 × 35.6 *cms.* Formerly called Linnell.
Purchased, 1950.

330 **A burning town by moonlight with travellers late-17th century**
Canvas 67.2 × 43.2 *cms.*
Purchased, 1950.

354 **Virgin and Child, whole length, with a bed behind**
Canvas 113 × 89 *cms.* From Italian late-16th century pattern.
Burton Bequest, 1882.

374 **Virgin and Child with St. John 17th century**
Panel 118.1 × 90.2 *cms.* Possibly Spanish colonial work.

388 **Diogenes in his barrel 17th century**
Canvas 170 × 182 *cms.* Formerly called 'Lucas de Edey 1668'.
Presented by Dr. T. Spinks, 1889.

389 **The Bass Rock with shipping c.1830**
Canvas 142.2 × 210.5 *cms.*
Acquired from Mrs. Bates before 1941.

390 **Coast scene with boats being unloaded 18th century**
Canvas 115.6 × 142.2 *cms.,* initialled *S A* (?).

391 **Saints Peter and John in the tombs**
Canvas 233.7 × 172.7 *cms.* In ruinous condition.
Burton Bequest, 1882.

414 **Infant Christ reclining on a cushion with raised arms**
Canvas 63.5 × 47 *cms.* From an Italian 17th-century pattern; formerly called
a Cupid after Guido Reni.
Burton Bequest, 1882.

428 **Peasants gaming 19th century**
Canvas 37.2 × 29.2 cms., initialled *MD^t M* (?).

460 **Interior of the Assembly Rooms, York**
Canvas 178 × 213.4 *cms.* From the 1759 engraving by W. Lindley.

465 **Two Dutch peasant women smoking**
Canvas 101.6 × 78.7 *cms.*

470 **The Doctor's Shop 17th century**
Canvas 64.5 × 81 *cms.* In the manner of Teniers.
Rawdon Bequest, 1895.

503   **St. Jerome   17th century**
Panel 32.4 × 23.2 *cms.*
Purchased, 1948.

567   **Acomb Green, York; the view from my window   c.1880**
Canvas 61 × 40.6 *cms.*
Presented by Mr. Hardcastle of York, 1951.

595   **Landscape with trees and a rocky stream   c.1840**
Millboard 17.8 × 29 *cms.*

598   **Samson bursting his bonds before Delilah   early-18th century**
Canvas 61 × 76.2 *cms.*   Possibly from a Venetian pattern.

975   **Landscape with figures   17th century**
Copper 17.2 × 22.9 *cms.*   Formerly attributed to Lucas van Uden.
Purchased, 1961.

1087   **A Beggar   early-19th century**
Canvas 76.2 × 61 *cms.*
Presented by D. G. Champion, 1964.

1099   **A young Girl in a hat   c.1840**
Canvas 68.6 × 53.4 *cms.*   Illus., *Preview,* 71, 1965, cover.
Purchased, 1964.

1103   **Reclining nude (recto); Cottage amongst trees (verso)   20th century**
Canvas 76.2 × 101.6 *cms.*
Presented by W. H. Vine, 1965.

1172   **A Falcon on a gloved hand   1677**
Canvas 66 × 49.5 *cms.,* inscribed *MI* and dated. A similar composition is at
Newburgh Priory.
Presented by Mrs. V. I. C. Knox, 1969.

1213   **Bas relief of five Putti; grisaille sketch   c.1800**
Canvas 76.2 × 106.7 *cms.*
Transferred from the Yorkshire Museum, 1971.

1258   **Ruins of Lord Ingram's House from the Dean's Park, York   c.1780**
Panel 21.6 × 27.9 *cms.*
Transferred from the Mansion House, 1973.

1259   **Clifford's Tower and Castlegate Postern c.1830**
Panel 27.5 × 35.5 *cms.*
Transferred from the Mansion House, 1973.

1260   **Lendal Ferry, York   c.1800**
Panel 20.5 × 27 *cms.*
Transferred from the Mansion House, 1973.

1261   **Old Ouse Bridge from Skeldergate Postern   c.1800**
Panel 21 × 27 *cms.*
Transferred from the Mansion House, 1973.

1262   **St Mary's Abbey, York   c.1830**
Canvas 71 × 92 *cms.*
Evelyn Collection, 1934 (0.1).

INDICES

NUMERICAL CONCORDANCE

ACCESSION NUMBER	ARTIST	ACCESSION NUMBER	ARTIST
1	Watts	134	Moore, H.
2	Watts	135	Lupton
3	Watts	137	Moore, H.
4	Watts	138	Unknown
5	Verschuur	140	Moore, H.
7	Pryde	141	Lucas
8	Sickert	142	Collins, C.
9	Gosse	143	Walton, J.
10	Greaves	144	Walton, J. T.
13	Unknown	145	Walton, J. T.
14	Le Bas	146	Peel
19	Maufra	147	Herring and **Faed, T.**
20	Ribot, T-A.	148	Soord
23	Shannon	149	Lucas
24	Dupré	150	Nixon
26	Blanche	151	Walton, J.
27	Newton	152	Unknown
35	Maitland	153	Swallow
37	Wood	154	Seignac
38	Banting	155	Chambers
42	Walker	156	Armfield
43	Walker	157	Dillens
47	Wolmark	158	Stanier
48	Unknown	159	Weiser
60	Walton, J. T.	160	Johnston
61	Ihlee	163	Unknown
62	Bayes	164	Lenfant
63	Dunlop	166	Unknown
108	Midwood	167	Emmerson
112	Salmon	168	Woolmer
113	Bouguereau **after**	169	Joy
114	Cooper, J.	170	Haynes
115	Morrison	171	Raine
116	Mackenzie-**Smith**	172	Broadbridge
117	Wickham	174	dal Sole, after
118	Henshaw	175	Unknown
119	Knell	178	Unknown
120	McCulloch	179	Barthel
121	Gogin	180	Nicol
123	Unknown	181	Craig
125	Mulready, A. E.	182	Jack
126	Shayer	183	Moore, W.
127	Holland, John	184	Haughton
128	Gogin	185	Atkinson
129	Caymans	186	Unknown
130	Lucas	187	Chambers
131	Pasmore, D.	188	Innocenti
132	Bright	189	Terry

ACCESSION NUMBER	ARTIST
191	Swallow
192	Jack
193	Dawson, H.
195	Murray
196	Callow
197	Burr
198	Murray
199	Cobbett
200	Holder
202	Holder
203	Stone, M.
204	Unknown
205	Unknown
206	Swallow
207	Yglesias
208	Hillier
209	Gilman
210	Unknown
212	Unknown
213	Wright, J., imitator
214	Higgins
215	Gogin
217	Moore, W.
218	Moore, W.
219	Gogin
220	Moore, H.
221	Dadd
222	Unknown
223	Unknown
224	Unknown
225	Unknown
226	Unknown
227	Stapylton
228	Unknown
229	Unknown
230	Mostyn
233	Grimshaw
234	Grimshaw
236	Bright
237	Unknown
238	Lee
239	Meadows
240	Unknown
241	Lance
242	Bright
243	Holder
244	Beavis
245	Stocquart
246	Hardy
248	Rosa, called

ACCESSION NUMBER	ARTIST
249	Moore, H.
250	Pettinger
251	Garland
252	Dawson, H.
253	Moore, H.
254	Dukes
256	Pyne
257	Swallow
258	Fall
263	Unknown
264	Holder
265	Unknown
266	Lingelbach, manner of
267	Bright and Hill
268	Tuke
269	Pasmore, D.
271	Hardy
272	Dawson, H.
273	Manzoni
275	Pyne
276	Martinetti
277	Pascitti
278	Raine
279	Holder
280	Ansdell
281	Holder
282	Unknown
283	Soord
284	Pasmore, D.
285	Pickersgill
286	Unknown
287	Shackleton
288	Coomans
289	Townesend, M.
290	Carmichael
291	Spreat
292	Poole
293	Gill, Edmund
294	Bough
295	Stanfield, G. C.
296	Pettitt, C.
297	Collier
298	Holder
299	Holder
300	Brion
301	Cauwer
303	Unknown
304	Hugo
305	Bonington, after
306	Ward, M. T.

ACCESSION NUMBER	ARTIST	ACCESSION NUMBER	ARTIST
307	Unknown	363	Carmichael
308	Carabin	364	Unknown
309	Montague	366	Brook
310	Dyckmans	367	Guy
311	Carmichael	369	Marshall
312	Ranken	370	Soord
313	Stone, F.	371	Fall
314	Beyle	372	Terry
315	Cooper, T. S.	373	Rubens, after
316	Linnell	374	Unknown
317	Jack	375	Percy
318	Moore, H.	376	Till
319	Armfield	377	Guy
320	Waterlow	378	Raine
321	Windass	379	Cave
322	Shackleton	380	Unknown
324	Soord	381	Dubufe
325	Unknown	382	Windass
326	Meak	383	Knell
327	Walton, J. T.	384	Phillip
328	Craft	385	Dawson, H. T.
329	Unknown	386	Carmichael
330	Unknown	387	Shackleton
331	Unknown	388	Unknown
332	Claxton	389	Unknown
333	Westcott	390	Unknown
334	Walton, J. T.	391	Unknown
335	Morel	392	Vila, after
336	Titian, after	393	Watts
337	Ansdell and Frith	395	Jack
338	Wright, R.	398	Crawshaw
339	Smith, T. W.	400	Dudley
340	Bright and Henzell	401	Walton, J.
341	Anderson	402	Fall
342	Knowles	403	Ramsay
344	Moore, H.	404	Harrison
349	Ward, E. M.	410	Coria
350	Henzell	414	Unknown
351	Gilbert	415	Vinal
352	Moore, H.	416	Swanick
353	Willis	422	Ward, M. T.
354	Unknown	423	Ward, M. T.
355	Unknown	424	Townesend, M.
356	Haas	425	Haughton
357	Anderson	427	Ward, M. T.
358	Titian, after	428	Unknown
359	Unknown	429	Grey
360	Unknown	430	Soord
361	Raine	432	Smith (H. L. ?)
362	Raine	438	Barau

ACCESSION NUMBER	ARTIST	ACCESSION NUMBER	ARTIST
439	Gertler	598	Unknown
441	Ribot, T-A.	599	Pether, A., style of
443	Mulard	600	Unknown
447	Unknown	601	Unknown
452	Moore, H.	614	Spreat
453	Moore, H.	615	Masser
456	Holder	616	Bonvin
457	Unknown	633	Adler
458	Allori, after	640	Medley
459	Unknown	649	Cafe
460	Unknown	650	Walker
461	Daubigny	652	Barau
462	Cazin	656	Knight
463	Bissière	664	Lowry
465	Unknown	669	Maris, J.
466	Wyck	677	Brundrit
467	Grimshaw	682	Ribot, G.
468	Kessel	687	Lowry
470	Unknown	690	Grossmith
473	Van Dyck, after	698	Moore, A.
479	Barrett, attributed	699	Moore, A.
480	Hornibrook	700	Moore, A.
482	Raine	701	Moore, A.
483	M, S.	705	Townsend, W.
484	Bell	715	Potter
485	Hudson, B.	716	Rosoman
486	Unknown	725	Gilman
487	Bell	749	Rubens, after
488	Lowe	846	Gilman
493	Pasmore, D.	855	Ginner
494	Horsley	867	John, G.
495	Jack	868	Nash
497	Cooper, T. S.	870	Smith, M.
500	Collins, H.	872	Rosoman
502	Higgins	878	Platt
503	Unknown	879	Bissière
562	Mauve	882	Adams
566	Blanche	891	Ozenfant
567	Unknown	892	Adams
568	Beaumont	893	Courbet
570	Uhlman	894	Walker
573	Pasmore, V.	914	Rousseau
574	Maitland, ascribed	915	Yeats
575	Monticelli	917	Maitland
578	Holland, D.	918	Studd
580	Hirst	919	Steer
582	Piper	921	Studd
591	Sickert	922	Starr, ascribed
595	Unknown	923	McCall
597	Hulme	924	Sickert

ACCESSION NUMBER	ARTIST	ACCESSION NUMBER	ARTIST
928	Roelofs	1099	Unknown
934	Loiseau	1100	Mascall, after
937	Blacklock	1103	Unknown
941	Bomberg	1106	Unknown
942	Riopelle	1107	Unknown
956	Pannini, manner of	1108	Unknown
957	Carrière	1109	Rutson
958	Michel	1110	Unknown
960	Kneale	1111	Unknown
961	O'Conor	1112	Unknown
965	Hayden	1113	Unknown
967	Cano, called	1114	Unknown
971	Guillemet	1115	Unknown
975	Unknown	1116	Unknown
978	Herman	1117	Isabey
980	Cazin	1118	Pettitt, J.
987	Mackenzie	1121	Donnelly
1003	Wynter	1122	Bevan, O.
1009	Caloutsis	1124	Stothard, attributed
1010	Hill	1125	Partridge
1011	Hofland	1127	Paolini, after
1012	Carmichael	1130	Unknown
1013	Moore, H.	1141	Karlowska
1014	Herring, after	1144	Foster
1015	Jack	1146	Unknown
1020	Herbin	1148	Unknown
1025	Bower, after	1152	Amiconi
1026	Tonks	1154	Benjamin
1027	Steer	1156	M., C. A.
1028	Greaves	1158	Unknown
1029	Sickert	1160	Unknown
1030	Conder	1164	Fall
1031	Spencer	1168	Jackson, F. W.
1032	Steer	1171	Van Dyck, after
1033	Bouneau	1172	Unknown
1034	Roussel	1173	Whittle
1035	Gore	1190	Faed, John
1036	Guevara	1196	Guy
1037	Maitland	1197	Brook
1038	Armstrong	1198	Patten
1039	Armstrong	1199	Banks
1042	Leslie, R. C.	1200	Raine
1044	Sickert	1201	Walton, G.
1051	Unknown	1202	Earles
1055	Bomberg	1203	Mayer
1059	Diaz	1204	Batty
1060	Pericle	1205	Batty
1061	Pericle	1206	Howell
1087	Unknown	1207	Gotch
1095	O'Conor	1208	Unknown

ACCESSION NUMBER	ARTIST	ACCESSION NUMBER	ARTIST
1211	Brook	1256	Cave
1212	Brook	1257	Lycett
1213	Unknown	1258	Unknown
1214	Diaz	1259	Unknown
1221	Grant	1260	Unknown
1226	Knowles	1261	Unknown
1227	Knowles	1262	Unknown
1228	Fantin-Latour	1263	Masser
1230	Pyne	1264	Brook
1246	Valentine	1265	W., F.
1247	Ward, M. T. and Boddington	1266	Brook
1248	M., H.	1267	Brook
1249	Nicholson, G.	1269	Guy
1250	Nicholson, G.	1270	Unknown
1251	Nicholson, G.	1271	Fall
1252	Cave	1272	Unknown
1253	Cave	1273	Unknown
1254	Cave	1274	Monkhouse
1255	Cave		

INDEX OF PORTRAITS

INDEX OF TOPOGRAPHY

PLATES

[1221] GRANT.　The second Earl de Grey.

[241] LANCE.   Still life with dead game.

[1190] John FAED.   The Thirsty Customer.

[958] MICHEL. The Plain of St-Denis.

[1117] ISABEY.   Boat in a Storm.

6

[147] HERRING and Thomas FAED.   Barney, leave the girls alone!

[316] LINNELL.   The Harvest Cradle: noontide.

[384] PHILLIP. Collecting the Offering in a Scottish Kirk.

[349] E. M. WARD.   Hogarth's Studio in 1739.

[914] ROUSSEAU.   Landscape with red sunset.

[1059] DIAZ.   The Forest of Fontainebleau.

[461] DAUBIGNY. The Waterfall.

[893] COURBET. Swiss Landscape.

[299] HOLDER.   On the Yorkshire Coast.

[275] PYNE.   Venice with the Strada Ferrata from the Lagunes.

[562] MAUVE. On the Beach.

[669] Jacob MARIS. A Dutch Waterway.

[318] Henry MOORE. Crossing the Bar.

[383] KNELL.   Entering Portsmouth Harbour.

[616] BONVIN. Still life.

[20] A-T. RIBOT. Still life with jug.

[1228] FANTIN-LATOUR. Roses.

[1037] MAITLAND.   Cheyne Walk in sunshine.

[10] GREAVES.   Japanese figures on Chelsea Embankment.

[591] SICKERT. The Butcher's Shop.

[919] STEER. Boats on the beach, Southwold.

[698] MOORE.   A Venus.

[1032] STEER. Kimono.

[2] WATTS. Ararat.

[1] WATTS. Progress.

[1026] TONKS. The Toilet.

[1030] CONDER. Yport.

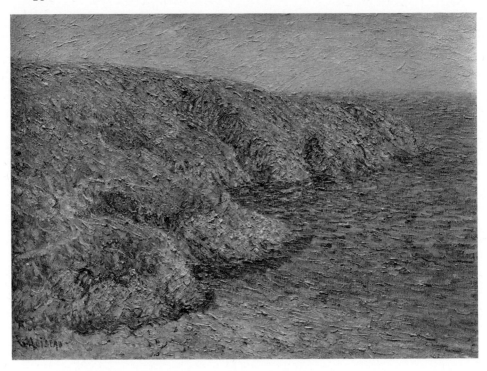

[934] LOISEAU. Port-de-Goulphar, Belle-Ile-en-Mer.

[1095] O'CONOR. The Wave.

[690] GROSSMITH.   Girl with a kettle.

[8] SICKERT. Old Heffel of Rowton House.

[924] SICKERT. The Visitor.

[1029] SICKERT.   The Piazzetta, Venice.

[209] GILMAN. The Artist's Daughters.

[725] GILMAN.   Interior with Nude.

[965] HAYDEN. St-Lunaire.

[891] OZENFANT.　Still life with jug.

[867] Gwen JOHN. Young woman in a red shawl.

[941] BOMBERG. Man's Head.

[868] Paul NASH. Winter Sea.

[1055] BOMBERG.   The Bath.

[1035] GORE.   From a canal bridge, Chalk Farm Road.

[582] PIPER.   Stair Hole, Lulworth.

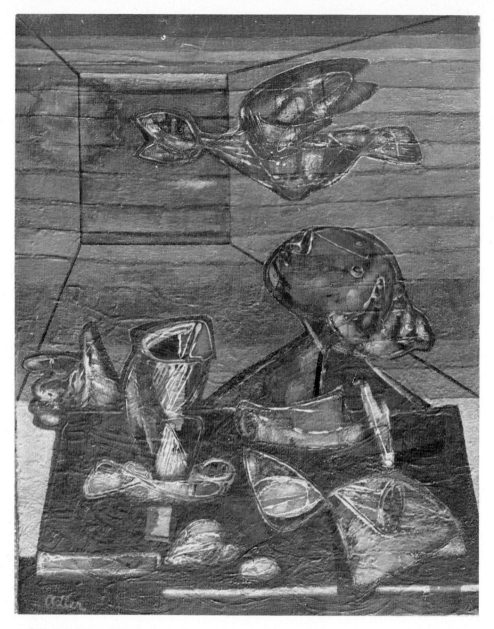

[633] ADLER. The Poet.

[1031] SPENCER.   The Deposition and Rolling Away of the Stone.

[915] YEATS. 'That we may never meet again'.